HYMNS

FOR JUNIOR WORSHIP

"I will sing of lovingkindness and justice:
Unto thee, O Lord, will I sing praises."
— *Ps. 101:1*

PHILADELPHIA
THE WESTMINSTER PRESS

"Hymns for Junior Worship" has been compiled by a committee of workers with children who have been deeply concerned about the Christian education of Junior boys and girls and eager to lead them into a rich experience of worship. This committee consists of the following persons:

MARIE C. DIETER
FLORENCE E. NORTON
PEARL ROSSER
JEAN M. STEWART
ELIZABETH F. TIBBALS
ELIZABETH S. WHITEHOUSE
BLANCHE HOKE, *Chairman*
LAWRENCE CURRY, *Musical Editor*

OUR THANKS

MANY people have helped to make this book. One man who gave a great deal of time and thought to it was Dr. Calvin W. Laufer. He tried to find out what kind of songs boys and girls enjoy, and he gathered together a great number from which to choose for this book. He died while the book was still being planned, but these pages express both his love for music and his love for boys and girls. Mr. Lawrence Curry, who works with Juniors, took over Dr. Laufer's work on this book. He helped us to choose songs and music; he wrote some of the music in this book. He wanted his music to be both beautiful to listen to and easy to sing.

Many other people helped to make this book, also. Marguerite de Angeli made the beautiful drawings we find in our book. A great number of the other helpers we do not know by name. Lumbermen and workers in a paper factory helped to make paper for the pages. Workers in a cloth factory helped to make the cloth with which the book is bound. Still other people helped to set the type for the pages, and run the printing presses, and do all the other work involved in printing a book. Train crews and plane crews, and perhaps boat crews too, helped to carry lumber and paper and metal and finally the finished books. We are grateful to all these people who made our book possible.

A number of these songs were written especially for this book. We want to thank the writers for the thoughtful and interested work they did.

Some of the words and music in this book are copyrighted, or owned, by certain companies or people, who have kindly let us use them. We want to thank them. In most cases, a note is placed at the bottom of a song, telling who owns the copyright for it and has given us permission to use it. All the hymns and tunes copyrighted by Dr. Calvin W. Laufer are used by permission of Mr. Edward B. Laufer. All the hymns and tunes copyrighted by Dr. Louis F. Benson are used by permission of Mrs. Robert F. Jefferys. If any material appears without proper acknowledgment this is to be taken as evidence that careful search is still being made to find the owners of copyrights, and that due credit will be given in future editions of the book.

THIS IS YOUR BOOK

EXPLORING THE BOOK

No one can use a book until he has learned to find his way about in it. This book was planned for you. Turn over the next page, and you will find a page headed "Songs and Other Music." Listed on that page are six sections into which the book is divided. Each section has a name, which you will recognize as coming from the Bible. The section name and the paragraph underneath it will help you to know the kind of songs that are in the section. This helps you to find what you want.

Let us suppose you have been out of doors on a wonderful day, and you want to sing how great God is who plans such days. To which section would you go for such a song? Wouldn't it be to Section 1, "Praise Ye the Lord"?

Suppose you have been studying about Jesus, and want to sing about him. To which section would you go to look for the songs? Wouldn't it be to Section 2, "He Loved Us, and Sent His Son"? Or suppose you want a prayer response for the worship service you are planning. You would turn to Section 6, "O Come, Let Us Worship."

Imagine some other times when you would want to sing. In each case try to decide where you would look for the songs.

FROM MANY LANDS

The words of the songs in this book, and the music too, come from many lands. You will find some from America, Austria, Denmark, England, France, Germany, Ireland, Italy, Scotland, Sweden, Wales; you will find Negro and Hebrew songs. Some are new, and some are very old.

Would you like to be able to discover for yourself where the songs come from, and how long ago they were written? Here is one way of doing so:

With each song, you will find a name or names at the left and also at the right side of the song, just below the title. The names at the left are those of the people who wrote the words. Often you can tell by the names what nationality the writers were. The date when they wrote is usually given, so you can tell how old the words are. Sometimes you will read that the words have been translated, which means they were first written in another language.

The names at the right side are those of the people who composed the music. Again you can often tell by the names what nationality the musician was. Sometimes you will find the name of a very old book in which the song appeared, such as the "Genevan Psalter." Where do you suppose that book was first used?

WHEN YOU SING

READING SONGS

Do you know how to read songs and music?

When you sing, you watch the top line of music, the line above the words. You don't pay any attention to the music just below the words. That is for the person who is playing the piano. The melody line, or line above the words, is for you. It tells you what notes to sing.

The words of the song have to be printed in a special way. You don't find poems printed that way except in a songbook.

Look at hymn number 1, "All People That on Earth Do Dwell." Notice that under the first line of music are three lines of words. The top line is numbered 1, the second line is numbered 2, and the third line is numbered 3. These are the numbers of the stanzas (sometimes wrongly called verses).

You start singing with the first stanza, the line numbered 1. It reads, "All people that on earth do dwell, Sing to the Lord with cheerful voice." When you have sung that line, you go to the first line in the second group of lines. You will find it under the second melody or singing line. You then sing, "Him serve with love, His praise forthtell, Come ye before Him and rejoice."

How does the second stanza read? the third?

PLANNING WORSHIP

When you plan worship services, or find songs for your own worship, you do not use just any hymns. You try to find hymns that say some of the things you are thinking about and will help you to worship at that time. You try to find hymns that have a connection with the thought around which the worship is planned.

By turning over the page, you will find a page headed "Songs and Other Music." This page gives you the names of the sections of music, and tells you the kind of songs or music in each section. That will help you to find what you want.

Or if you are looking for a certain hymn you know you want, turn to the back of the book. There you will find a list of the titles of the hymns, and the first lines. They are arranged in alphabetical order, and you look them up as you would look up a word in the dictionary. If a word or phrase is printed all in capital letters it means that that is the title of a hymn. When the words are printed with small letters it means that this is the first line of the hymn.

Worship is so important that it needs to be planned carefully, doesn't it? It is worth while to try to find just the songs and music that you need.

SONGS AND OTHER MUSIC

Section 1. "PRAISE YE THE LORD"   Hymns 1–28

Praise hymns, for general use when we worship. These praise God for his goodness and love, and his care for us. Some of them praise him for the world he has planned, for the seasons, or for the day or night.

Section 2. "HE LOVED US, AND SENT HIS SON"   Hymns 29–57

Hymns about Jesus. There are songs about the first Christmas, when Jesus was born, songs that tell how he grew up, and about the wonderful things he did for people. There are some Easter songs that tell of his death and resurrection.

Section 3. "LORD, I WOULD FOLLOW THEE"   Hymns 58–87

Hymns about us and how we may follow Christ or work with God. Hymns too about God's nearness and help are in this section. There are also prayer hymns.

Section 4. "INTO ALL THE WORLD"   Hymns 88–105

Hymns that tell of Christianity reaching out into all the world. Some of these hymns sing of our faith and our Church, and how the gospel is being carried to all the world. Some of them tell how people can make the world better when they have learned to live according to God's plan.

Section 5. "BLESSED IS THE NATION WHOSE GOD IS THE LORD"
Hymns 106–118

Hymns about our country and our cities. Thanksgiving and New Year hymns are in this section also.

Section 6. "O COME, LET US WORSHIP"   Hymns 119–148

Special worship materials. These include chants and responses which Junior choirs will find especially helpful. Instrumental music is to be found in this section, numbers 136–148. There are Scripture selections for use in worship on pages 138, 139.

All People That on Earth Do Dwell

OLD HUNDREDTH

William Kethe, 1561
Thomas Ken, 1692

Louis Bourgeois, "Genevan Psalter," 1551

1. All peo-ple that on earth do dwell, Sing to the Lord with cheer-ful voice;
2. For why? the Lord our God is good, His mer-cy is for-ev-er sure;
3. Praise God from whom all bless-ings flow; Praise Him, all crea-tures here be-low;

Him serve with love, His praise forth-tell, Come ye be-fore Him and re-joice.
His truth at all times firm-ly stood, And shall from age to age en-dure.
Praise Him a-bove, ye heaven-ly host: Praise Fa-ther, Son, and Ho-ly Ghost.

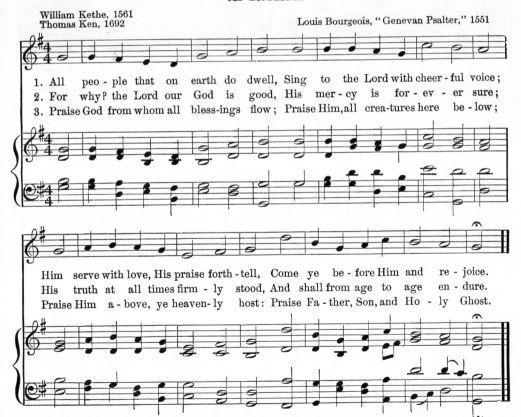

2

Morning Hymn

PARK

Louis F. Benson, 1897

Lawrence Curry, 1939

1. The sun is on the land and sea, The day be-gun;
2. Thy love was ev-er in our view, Like stars, by night;
3. We do not know what grief or care The day may bring:

Our morn-ing hymn be-gins with Thee, Blest Three in One;
Thy gifts are ev-ery morn-ing new, O God of light;
The heart shall find some glad-ness there That loves its King;

Our praise shall rise con-tin-ual-ly Till day is done.
Thy mer-cy, like the heav-ens' blue, Fills all our sight.
The life that serves Thee ev-ery-where Can al-ways sing.

A Song of Thanksgiving

WENTWORTH

Adelaide A. Procter, 1858

Frederick C. Maker, 1876

1. My God, I thank Thee, who hast made The earth so bright,
2. I thank Thee, too, that Thou hast made Joy to a - bound;
3. I thank Thee, Lord, that Thou hast kept The best in store;

So full of splen - dor and of joy, Beau - ty and light;
So man - y gen - tle thoughts and deeds Cir - cling us round,
We have e - nough, yet not too much To long for more:

So man - y glo - rious things are here, No - ble and right.
That in the dark - est spot of earth Some love is found.
A yearn - ing for a deep - er peace Not known be - fore.

4 We Sing Our Praise

Nancy Byrd Turner, 1926

Karl P. Harrington, 1926

1. When light is in the morn - ing sky, When dusk is
2. For life up - on the love - ly earth, And guid - ing

calm and fair, At noon, at night, we bow our heads
all our days; For love and home and all our joys

And lift our hearts in prayer. We speak to God and
To God we sing our praise. In ear - nest hymn and

know our word At an - y hour of need is heard.
hap - py song We lift our thanks the whole year long.

rit.

May Jesus Christ Be Praised

LAUDES DOMINI

Anon. (German, c. 1800)
Trans. by Edward Caswall, 1853, 1858

Joseph Barnby, 1868

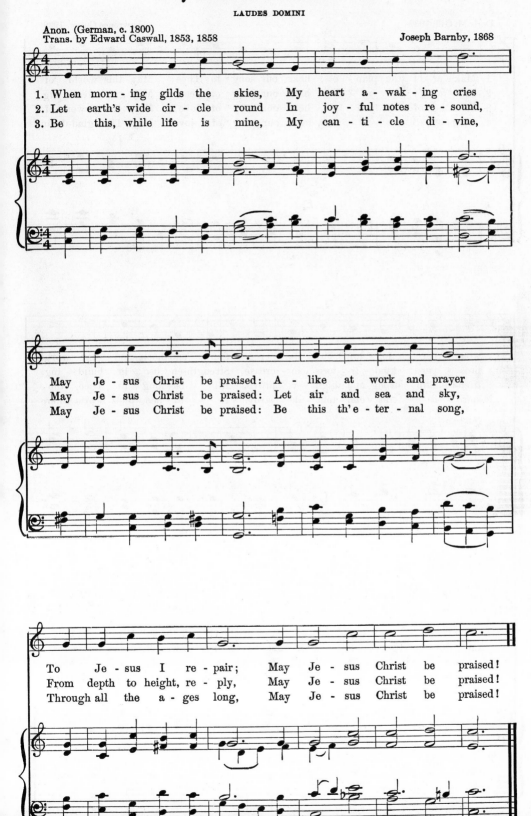

1. When morn-ing gilds the skies, My heart a-wak-ing cries
2. Let earth's wide cir-cle round In joy-ful notes re-sound,
3. Be this, while life is mine, My can-ti-cle di-vine,

May Je-sus Christ be praised: A-like at work and prayer
May Je-sus Christ be praised: Let air and sea and sky,
May Je-sus Christ be praised: Be this th'e-ter-nal song,

To Je-sus I re-pair; May Je-sus Christ be praised!
From depth to height, re-ply, May Je-sus Christ be praised!
Through all the a-ges long, May Je-sus Christ be praised!

Maker of the Planets

HOKE

Doris M. Gill, 1939

Lawrence Curry, 1939

1. Mak - er of the plan - ets, hear our song to Thee: May this world of
2. Rul - er of the na - tions, hear our song of peace: May good feel - ing
3. Fa - ther of all peo - ple, hear our song of love: May the power of
4. King of all cre - a - tion, hear our song of joy: May Thy glad-dening

won - der fol - low Thy de - cree. Sun and moon and star - worlds
pros - per, kind - li - ness in - crease. Strength-en us in build - ing
friend - ship strong and might - y prove. All be - long to Thee, the
spir - it dis - con - tent de - stroy. In - to peo - ple's hearts where

cease - less - ly o - bey; May we heed Thee faith - ful - ly as they.
brid - ges of good will; Men shall yet Thy laws of peace ful - fill.
dusk - y and the fair; Teach us all things e - qual - ly to share.
may be fear or pain, King of glo - ry, en - ter in and reign.

My God and King

ALL THE WORLD

George Herbert (1593–1632); alt.

Robert G. McCutchan, 1934

1. Let all the world in ev-ery cor-ner sing, "My God and King!"
2. Let all the world in ev-ery cor-ner sing, "My God and King!"

The heavens are not too high, His praise may thith-er fly; The
The Church with psalms must shout, No door can keep them out; But

earth is not too low, His prais-es there may grow. Let
more than all the heart Must bear the lar-gest part. Let

all the world in ev-ery cor-ner sing, "My God and King!"

O Worship the King

LYONS

Psalm 104
Robert Grant, 1833

Arr. from J. Michael Haydn (1737–1806)

1. O wor-ship the King all glo-rious a-bove, O grate-ful-ly sing His
2. The earth with its store of won-ders un-told, Al-might-y, Thy power hath
3. Thy boun-ti-ful care what tongue can re-cite? It breathes in the air, it

power and His love; Our Shield and De-fend-er, the An-cient of Days,
found-ed of old; Hath stab-lished it fast by a change-less de-cree,
shines in the light; It streams from the hills, it de-scends to the plain,

Pa-vil-ioned in splen-dor, and gird-ed with praise.
And round it hath cast, like a man-tle, the sea.
And sweet-ly dis-tills in the dew and the rain.

Holy, Holy, Holy! Lord God Almighty

NICAEA

Reginald Heber, 1826; alt.

John B. Dykes, 1861

1. Ho - ly, Ho - ly, Ho - ly! Lord God Al - might - y!
2. Ho - ly, Ho - ly, Ho - ly! Lord God Al - might - y!

Ear - ly in the morn - ing our song shall rise to Thee;
All Thy works shall praise Thy Name, in earth and sky and sea;

Ho - ly, Ho - ly, Ho - ly! Mer - ci - ful and Might - y!
Ho - ly, Ho - ly, Ho - ly! Mer - ci - ful and Might - y!

Per - fect in power, in love, and pu - ri - ty.
Per - fect in power, in love, and pu - ri - ty.

10   A Jewish Festival Song

CHANUKAH HYMN

Translated from the
German of Leopold Stein by
M. Jastrow and G. Gottheil

Traditional

1. Rock of A - ges, let our song Praise Thy sav - ing pow - er;
2. Kin - dling new the ho - ly lamps, Priests ap - proved in suf - fer - ing,
3. Chil - dren of the mar - tyr race, Wheth - er free or fet - tered,

Thou, a - midst the ra - ging foes, Wast our shel - ter - ing tow - er.
Pu - ri - fied the na - tion's shrine, Brought to God their of - fer - ing.
Wake the ech - oes of the songs Where ye may be scat - tered!

Fu - rious they as - sailed us, But Thine arm a - vailed us,
And His courts sur - round - ing Hear, in joy a - bound - ing,
Yours the mes - sage cheer - ing, That the time is near - ing

And Thy word Broke their sword, When our own strength failed us.
Hap - py throngs Sing - ing songs Far and wide re - sound - ing.
Which shall see All men free, Ty - rants dis - ap - pear - ing!

From "The Ceremonies of Judaism." Copyright, 1930, by the National Federation of Temple Brotherhoods.

NOTE: The Jews call this hymn "Rock of Ages." It was written in memory of the day when the Temple was saved from enemies.

The God of Abraham Praise

LEONI

Daniel Ben Judah, 14th century
Revised version of " The Yigdal."

Hebrew Melody

1. The God of Abra - ham praise, All prais - ed be His Name,
2. His spir - it flow - eth free High sur - ging where it will:
3. He hath e - ter - nal life Im - plant - ed in the soul;

Who was, and is, and is to be, And still the same!
In proph - et's word He spoke of old— He speak - eth still.
His love shall be our strength and stay, While a - ges roll.

The one e - ter - nal God, Ere aught that now ap - pears;
Es - tab - lished is His law, And change-less it shall stand,
Praise to the liv - ing God! All prais - ed be His Name,

The First, the Last: be - yond all thought His time - less years!
Deep writ up - on the hu - man heart, On sea or land.
Who was, and is, and is to be, And still the same!

12 Joyful, Joyful, We Adore Thee

HYMN TO JOY

Henry van Dyke, 1907

Arr. from Beethoven, 1824

With spirit

1. Joy-ful, joy-ful, we a-dore Thee, God of glo-ry, Lord of love;
2. All Thy works with joy sur-round Thee, Earth and heaven re-flect Thy rays,
3. Thou art giv-ing and for-giv-ing, Ev-er bless-ing, ev-er blest,
4. Mor-tals, join the might-y cho-rus Which the morn-ing stars be-gan;

Hearts un-fold like flowers be-fore Thee, Prais-ing Thee their Sun a-bove.
Stars and an-gels sing a-round Thee, Cen-ter of un-bro-ken praise.
Well-spring of the joy of liv-ing, O-cean depth of hap-py rest!
Fa-ther love is reign-ing o'er us, Broth-er love binds man to man.

Melt the clouds of sin and sad-ness, Drive the dark of doubt a-way;
Field and for-est, vale and moun-tain, Bloom-ing mead-ow, flash-ing sea,
Thou our Fa-ther, Christ our Broth-er, All who live in love are Thine;
Ev-er sing-ing, march we on-ward, Vic-tors in the midst of strife,

Giv-er of im-mor-tal glad-ness, Fill us with the light of day.
Chant-ing bird and flow-ing foun-tain, Call us to re-joice in Thee.
Teach us how to love each oth-er, Lift us to the Joy di-vine.
Joy-ful mu-sic lifts us Sun-ward In the tri-umph song of life.

Come, Thou Almighty King

TRINITY

Anon., c. 1757

Felice de Giardini, 1769

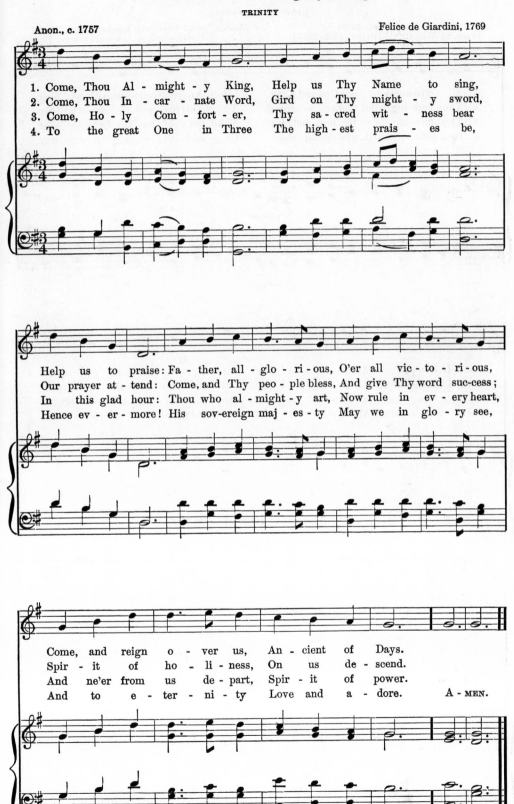

1. Come, Thou Al - might - y King, Help us Thy Name to sing,
2. Come, Thou In - car - nate Word, Gird on Thy might - y sword,
3. Come, Ho - ly Com - fort - er, Thy sa - cred wit - ness bear
4. To the great One in Three The high - est prais - es be,

Help us to praise: Fa - ther, all - glo - ri - ous, O'er all vic - to - ri - ous,
Our prayer at - tend: Come, and Thy peo - ple bless, And give Thy word suc - cess;
In this glad hour: Thou who al - might - y art, Now rule in ev - ery heart,
Hence ev - er - more! His sov-ereign maj - es - ty May we in glo - ry see,

Come, and reign o - ver us, An - cient of Days.
Spir - it of ho - li - ness, On us de - scend.
And ne'er from us de - part, Spir - it of power.
And to e - ter - ni - ty Love and a - dore. A - MEN.

14 All Creatures of Our God and King

LASST UNS ERFREUEN

St. Francis of Assisi (1182–1226)
Trans. by William H. Draper (1855–1933)

Melody from "Geistliche Kirchengesäng," 1623
Harmonized by Lawrence Curry, 1939

1. All crea-tures of our God and King, Lift up your voice and with us sing,
2. Thou rush-ing wind that art so strong, Ye clouds that sail in heaven a-long,
3. Thou flow-ing wa-ter, pure and clear, Make mu-sic for Thy Lord to hear,
4. Dear moth-er earth, who day by day Un-fold-est bless-ings on our way,

Al-le-lu-ia! Al-le-lu-ia! Thou burn-ing sun with gold-en beam,
O praise Him! Al-le-lu-ia! Thou ris-ing morn in praise re-joice,
Al-le-lu-ia! Al-le-lu-ia! Thou fire so mas-ter-ful and bright,
O praise Him! Al-le-lu-ia! The flowers and fruits that in thee grow,

Thou sil-ver moon with soft-er gleam! O praise Him, O praise Him!
Ye lights of eve-ning find a voice! O praise Him, O praise Him!
Thou giv-est man both warmth and light! O praise Him, O praise Him!
Let them His glo-ry al-so show! O praise Him, O praise Him!

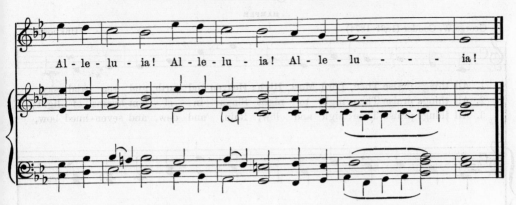

Al - le - lu - ia! Al - le - lu - ia! Al - le - lu - - - ia!

5. And all ye men of tender heart,
   Forgiving others, take your part.
      O sing ye! Alleluia!
   Ye who long pain and sorrow bear,
   Praise God and on Him cast your care!
      O praise Him! Alleluia!

6. Let all things their Creator bless,
   And worship Him in humbleness.
      O praise Him! Alleluia!
   Praise, praise the Father, praise the Son,
   And praise the Spirit, Three in One!
      O praise Him! Alleluia!

Words by permission, from Curwen Edition No. 80649, published by J. Curwen & Sons, Ltd., 24 Berners Street, London, W. 1, England. One stanza is omitted by their consent.
Music copyright, 1940, by Presbyterian Board of Christian Education.

All That's Good, and Great, and True   15

ORIENTIS PARTIBUS

Godfrey Thring

Medieval French Melody
Attributed to Pierre de Corbeil

1. All that's good, and great, and true, All that is and is to be,
2. Not a bird that doth not sing Sweet - est prais - es to Thy Name;
3. Ev - ery blade and ev - ery tree, All in hap - py con - cert ring,
4. Fill us, then, with love di - vine; Grant that we, though toil - ing here,

Be it old or be it new, Comes, O Fa - ther, comes from Thee.
Not an in - sect on the wing But Thy won - ders doth pro - claim.
And in won - drous har - mo - ny Join in prais - es to their King.
May in spir - it, be - ing Thine, See and hear Thee ev - ery - where. A - MEN.

16

All Things Praise Thee

HARPER

George W. Conder (1821–1874)

Unknown

1. All things praise Thee, Lord Most High: Heaven and earth, and sea and sky,
2. All things praise Thee: night to night Sings in si - lent hymns of light;
3. All things praise Thee: high and low, Rain, and dew, and seven-hued bow,

All were for Thy glo - ry made, That Thy great - ness, thus dis - played,
All things praise Thee: day to day Chants Thy power in burn - ing ray;
Crim-son sun - set, flee - cy cloud, Rip - pling stream, and tem - pest loud,

Should all wor - ship bring to Thee; All things praise Thee: Lord, may we.
Time and space are prais - ing Thee; All things praise Thee: Lord, may we.
Sum - mer, win - ter—all to Thee Glo - ry ren - der: Lord, may we.

This Is My Father's World

TERRA BEATA

Maltbie D. Babcock, 1901   Franklin L. Sheppard, 1915

Joyously

1. This is my Fa - ther's world, And to my lis - tening ears,
2. This is my Fa - ther's world, The birds their car - ols raise,

All na - ture sings, and round me rings The mu - sic of the spheres.
The morn - ing light, the lil - y white, De - clare their Mak - er's praise.

This is my Fa - ther's world: I rest me in the thought
This is my Fa - ther's world: He shines in all that's fair;

Of rocks and trees, of skies and seas; His hand the won - ders wrought.
In the rus - tling grass I hear Him pass, He speaks to me ev - ery - where.

With Happy Voices Ringing

TOURS

William G. Tarrant, 1888

Berthold Tours, 1872

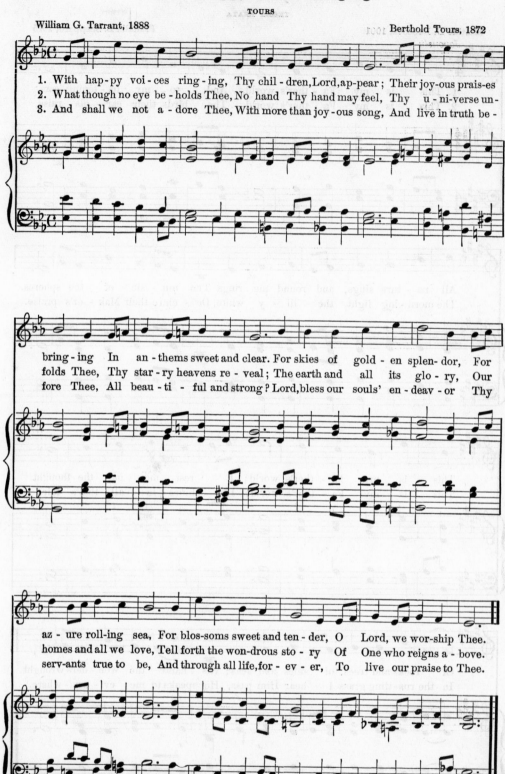

1. With hap-py voi-ces ring-ing, Thy chil-dren, Lord, ap-pear; Their joy-ous prais-es bring-ing In an-thems sweet and clear. For skies of gold-en splen-dor, For az-ure roll-ing sea, For blos-soms sweet and ten-der, O Lord, we wor-ship Thee.

2. What though no eye be-holds Thee, No hand Thy hand may feel, Thy u-ni-verse un-folds Thee, Thy star-ry heavens re-veal; The earth and all its glo-ry, Our homes and all we love, Tell forth the won-drous sto-ry Of One who reigns a-bove.

3. And shall we not a-dore Thee, With more than joy-ous song, And live in truth be-fore Thee, All beau-ti-ful and strong? Lord, bless our souls' en-deav-or Thy serv-ants true to be, And through all life, for-ev-er, To live our praise to Thee.

DEO GRATIAS

Margaret Sangster, 1893

A. B. Ponsonby, 1913

1. The ships glide in at the har-bor's mouth, And the ships sail out to sea,
2. The har-vest waves in the breez-y morn, And the men go forth to reap;

And the wind that sweeps from the sun-ny south Is sweet as sweet can be.
The full-ness comes to the tas-seled corn, Wheth-er we wake or sleep.

There's a world of toil and a world of pains, And a world of trou-ble and care,
And far on the hills by feet un-trod There are blos-soms that scent the air,

But O in a world where our Fa-ther reigns, There is glad-ness ev-ery-where!
For O in this world of our Fa-ther, God, There is beau-ty ev-ery-where!

" Lo, the Winter Is Past "

Song of Solomon 2: 11, 12

Edward Shippen Barnes

Moderato

Lo, the win - ter is past; The rain is o - ver and

gone; The flowers ap - pear on the earth; The time of the sing-ing of

birds is come.

21

The Glory of the Spring

SOHO

Arr. from Thomas H. Gill, 1867

Joseph Barnby, 1881

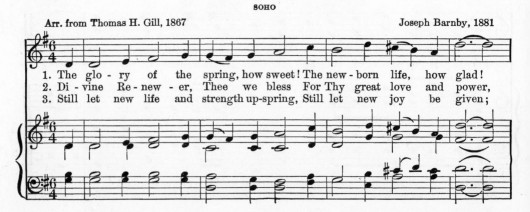

1. The glo - ry of the spring, how sweet! The new - born life, how glad!
2. Di - vine Re - new - er, Thee we bless For Thy great love and power,
3. Still let new life and strength up-spring, Still let new joy be given;

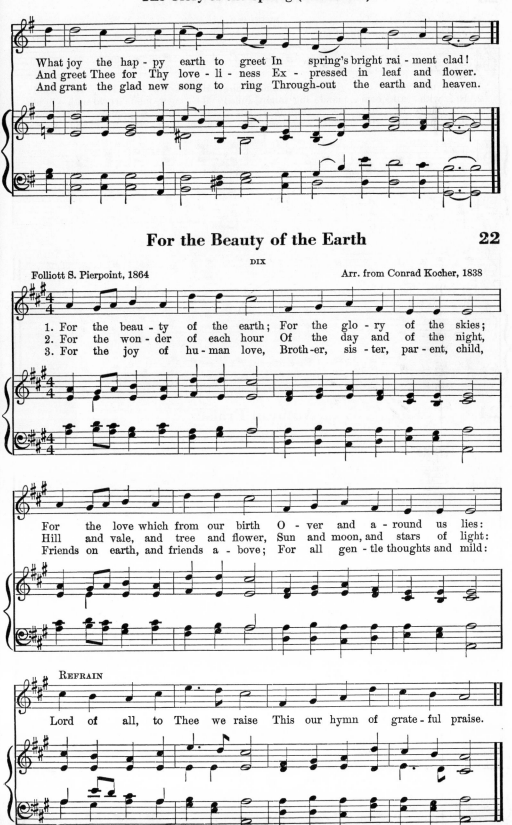

What joy the hap-py earth to greet In spring's bright rai-ment clad!
And greet Thee for Thy love-li-ness Ex-pressed in leaf and flower.
And grant the glad new song to ring Through-out the earth and heaven.

For the Beauty of the Earth 22

DIX

Folliott S. Pierpoint, 1864

Arr. from Conrad Kocher, 1838

1. For the beau-ty of the earth; For the glo-ry of the skies;
2. For the won-der of each hour Of the day and of the night,
3. For the joy of hu-man love, Broth-er, sis-ter, par-ent, child,

For the love which from our birth O-ver and a-round us lies:
Hill and vale, and tree and flower, Sun and moon, and stars of light:
Friends on earth, and friends a-bove; For all gen-tle thoughts and mild:

REFRAIN

Lord of all, to Thee we raise This our hymn of grate-ful praise.

Ever Faithful, Ever Sure

MONKLAND

Psalm 136. John Milton, 1624; alt.

Arr. by John B. Wilkes, 1861

1. Let us with a glad-some mind Praise the Lord, for He is kind:
2. He, with all-com-mand-ing might, Filled the new-made world with light:
3. All things liv-ing He doth feed; His full hand sup-plies their need:
4. Let us, then, His praise sing forth, His high maj-es-ty and worth:

For His mer-cies aye en-dure, Ev-er faith-ful, ev-er sure.

24

Autumn Praise

PLEYEL'S HYMN

Anna L. Barbauld, 1772; alt.

Arr. from Ignaz J. Pleyel, 1790

1. Praise to God, im-mor-tal praise, For the love that crowns our days:
2. All the plen-ty sum-mer pours; Au-tumn's rich o'er-flow-ing stores;
3. All to Thee, our God, we owe, Source whence all our bless-ings flow;
4. As Thy pros-pering hand hath blest, May we give Thee of our best;

Boun-teous Source of ev-ery joy, Let Thy praise our tongues em-ploy.
Flocks that whit-en all the plain; Yel-low sheaves of rip-ened grain:
Sing-ing thus through all our days, Praise to God, im-mor-tal praise.
And by deeds of kind-ly love For Thy mer-cies grate-ful prove.

The March of Days

BETHLEHEM

Frances Whitmarsh Wile, 1912

Gottfried W. Fink, 1842

1. All beau - ti - ful the march of days, As sea - sons come and go;
2. O'er white ex - pans - es spar - kling pure The ra - diant morns un - fold;
3. O Thou from whose un - fath - omed law The year in beau - ty flows,

The Hand that shaped the rose hath wrought The crys - tal of the snow;
The sol - emn splen - dors of the night Burn bright - er through the cold;
Thy - self the vi - sion pass - ing by In crys - tal and in rose,

Hath sent the hoar - y frost of heaven, The flow - ing wa - ters sealed,
Life mounts in ev - ery throb - bing vein, Love deep - ens round the hearth,
Day un - to day doth ut - ter speech, And night to night pro - claim,

And laid a si - lent love - li - ness On hill and wood and field.
And clear - er sounds the an - gel hymn, "Good will to men on earth."
In ev - er - chan - ging words of light, The won - der of Thy Name.

Words used by permission of Dorothy M. W. Bean.

In Summer Fields

KIRK

Doris M. Gill, 1938

Lawrence Curry, 1939

1. In sum-mer fields are grass-es green Which rip-ple like the seas,
2. In woods where squir-rels dart and spring Are trees as tall as towers,
3. In lands which lie be-yond the sea Are moun-tains capped with snow,
4. Then let us ren-der thanks to God, And let us all con-fess

And flowers as thick as stars at night, And but-ter-flies and bees;
And many a bough with leaf-y twigs A round-ed nest em-bowers.
And pools where rein-deer come to drink, And bear and buf-fa-lo;
That none but He could form a world So full of love-li-ness.

While o-ver-head the rob-in sings, Up soars the tire-less lark,
Here flies the mag-pie to and fro, The wood-peck-er and the rook;
And or-ange groves and pad-dy fields, And crags where ea-gles range,
To Him who made all things that be, Yet noth-ing made the same,

In Summer Fields (concluded)

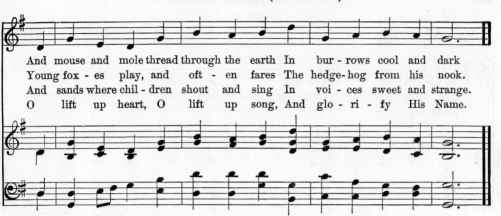

And mouse and mole thread through the earth In bur - rows cool and dark
Young fox - es play, and oft - en fares The hedge - hog from his nook.
And sands where chil - dren shout and sing In voi - ces sweet and strange.
O lift up heart, O lift up song, And glo - ri - fy His Name.

Alternative tune, " Materna," number 108.

Now the Day Is Over 27

ARMENTROUT

Sabine Baring–Gould, 1865
Two stanzas omitted

Calvin W. Laufer, 1921

1. Now the day is o - ver, Night is draw - ing nigh,
2. Je - sus, give the wea - ry Calm and sweet re - pose;
3. Grant to lit - tle chil - dren Vi - sions bright of Thee;
4. Com - fort ev - ery suf - ferer Watch - ing late in pain;

Shad - ows of the eve - ning Steal a - cross the sky.
With Thy ten - derest bless - ing May mine eye - lids close.
Guard the sail - ors toss - ing On the deep blue sea.
Those who plan some e - vil From their sin re - strain. A - MEN.

5. When the morning wakens,
   Then may I arise
   Pure, and fresh, and sinless
   In Thy holy eyes.

6. Glory to the Father,
   Glory to the Son,
   And to Thee, blest Spirit,
   Whilst all ages run.

Evening Prayer

AR HYD Y NOS

Reginald Heber (1783–1826)
William Mercer, 1864

Welsh Traditional Melody
Harmonized by L. O. Emerson, 1906

1. God, that mad-est earth and heav-en, Dark-ness and light;
2. And when morn a-gain shall call us To run life's way,

Who the day for toil hast giv-en, For rest the night;
May we still, what-e'er be-fall us, Thy will o-bey.

May Thine an-gel guards de-fend us, Slum-ber sweet Thy mer-cy send us;
From the power of e-vil hide us, In the nar-row path-way guide us,

Ho-ly dreams and hopes at-tend us, This live-long night.
Nor Thy smile be e'er de-nied us The live-long day. A-MEN.

He Loved Us and Sent His Son

Praise to God in Heaven

PUER NOBIS

"Piae Cantiones," 1582
Harmonized by Lawrence Curry

Lawrence Curry, 1939

1. Once for us a Boy was born, Joy and glad-ness bring - ing; Long a - go on
2. In the fields the shep-herds lay, Watch-ing sheep so low - ly; Till in vast and
3. As the Ma - gi did of old, So we bring our treas - ure; Gifts of self as
4. Come ye all and praise this Boy, Born the King of glo - ry; Sing ye now in

Christ-mas morn, Both heaven and earth were sing - ing Praise to God in heav - en!
bright ar - ray Ap - peared the an - gels ho - ly. Praise to God in heav - en!
well as gold To Him in full - est meas - ure. Praise to God in heav - en!
great - est joy Sal - va - tion's glo - rious sto - ry, Praise to God in heav - en!

30 O Come, O Come, Emmanuel

VENI EMMANUEL

From the Latin, 12th century
Stanza 1 trans. by John M. Neale, 1851
Stanzas 2, 3 trans. by Henry S. Coffin (1877–   )

Ancient Plain Song
13th century

1. O come, O come, Em - man - u - el, And ran - som cap - tive
2. O come, Thou Wis - dom from on high, And or - der all things
3. O come, De - sire of na - tions, bind All peo - ples in one

Is - ra - el, That mourns in lone - ly ex - ile here
far and nigh; To us the path of knowl - edge show,
heart and mind; Bid en - vy, strife, and quar - rels cease;

Un - til the Son of God ap - pear. Re - joice! Re - joice!
And cause us in her ways to go. Re - joice! Re - joice!
Fill the whole world with heav - en's peace. Re - joice! Re - joice!

Em - man - u - el Shall come to thee, O Is - ra - el!

When Christ Was Born   31

LUTE-BOOK LULLABY

From W. Ballet's "Lute Book," 17th century
Arr. by Lawrence Curry

Harleian MS., 1456; alt.

1. When Christ was born of Ma - ry free In Beth - le - hem, that fair cit - y,
2. The herds-men be-held those an - gels bright, To them ap - pear-ing with great light,
3. This King is come to save man-kind, In Scrip-ture prom-ised as we find.
4. Grant us, O Lord, for Thy great grace, In heaven the bliss to see Thy face,

The an - gels sang with mirth and glee, "In ex - cel - sis glo - ri - a."
And said, "God's Son is born this night, In ex - cel - sis glo - ri - a."
We there - fore have this song in mind: "In ex - cel - sis glo - ri - a."
That we may sing to Thy sol - ace: "In ex - cel - sis glo - ri - a."

32 Christians, Awake!

YORKSHIRE

John Byrom, 1750

John Wainwright, 1760

1. Chris - tians, a - wake! Sa - lute the hap - py morn, Where - on the
2. Then to the watch - ful shep - herds it was told, Who heard th' an -
3. He spake: and straight - way the ce - les - tial choir In hymns of

Sav-iour of the world was born; Rise to a - dore the mys-ter - y of love,
gel - ic her-ald's voice:"Be - hold, I bring good ti - dings of a Sav-iour's birth
joy, un-known be -fore, con - spire; The prais - es of re - deem-ing love they sang,

Which hosts of an - gels chant-ed from a - bove; With them the joy - ful
To you, and all the na - tions up - on earth: This day hath God ful -
And heaven's whole orb with al - le - lu - ias rang: God's high - est glo - ry

ti - dings first be - gun Of God In - car - nate and the Vir - gin's Son.
filled His prom - ised word; This day is born a Sav-iour, Christ the Lord."
was their an - them still, Peace up - on earth, and un - to men good will.

O Come, All Ye Faithful

ADESTE FIDELES

Anon. (Latin, 18th century)
Trans. by Frederick Oakeley, 1841

J. F. Wade's " Cantus Diversi," 1751

1. O come, all ye faith - ful, Joy - ful and tri - um - phant, O come ye, O
2. Sing, choirs of an - gels, Sing in ex - ul - ta - tion; Sing, all ye
3. Yea, Lord, we greet Thee, Born this hap - py morn - ing: Je - sus, to

come ye to Beth - le - hem; Come and be - hold Him
cit - i - zens of heaven a - bove; Glo - ry to God
Thee be glo - ry given; Word of the Fa - ther,

REFRAIN

Born the King of an - gels; O come, let us a - dore Him, O come, let
In the high - est;
Late in flesh ap - pear - ing;

us a - dore Him, O come, let us a - dore Him, Christ the Lord.

It Came Upon the Midnight Clear

CAROL

Edmund H. Sears, 1850

Richard S. Willis, 1850

1. It came up-on the mid-night clear, That glo-rious song of old,
2. Still through the clo-ven skies they come, With peace-ful wings un-furled,
3. And ye, be-neath life's crush-ing load, Whose forms are bend-ing low,
4. For lo, the days are has-tening on, By proph-et bards fore-told,

From an-gels bend-ing near the earth, To touch their harps of gold:
And still their heaven-ly mu-sic floats O'er all the wea-ry world:
Who toil a-long the climb-ing way With pain-ful steps and slow,
When with the ev-er-cir-cling years Comes round the age of gold;

"Peace on the earth, good will to men, From heaven's all-gra-cious King":
A-bove its sad and low-ly plains They bend on hov-ering wing,
Look now! for glad and gold-en hours Come swift-ly on the wing:
When peace shall o-ver all the earth Its an-cient splen-dors fling,

The world in sol-emn still-ness lay, To hear the an-gels sing.
And ev-er o'er its Ba-bel sounds The bless-ed an-gels sing.
O rest be-side the wea-ry road, And hear the an-gels sing.
And the whole world give back the song Which now the an-gels sing.

Silent Night! Holy Night!

STILLE NACHT

Joseph Mohr, 1818

Franz Grüber, 1818

1. Si - lent night! ho - ly night! All is dark, save the light
2. Peace - ful night! ho - li - est night! Dark - ness flies, all is light;
3. Si - lent night! ho - ly night! Guid - ing star, lend thy light!
4. Si - lent night! ho - li - est night! Won - drous star, lend thy light!

Yon - der, where they sweet vig - il keep O'er the Babe, who in si - lent sleep
Shep - herds hear the an - gels sing: "Al - le - lu - ia! hail the King!
See the East - ern Wise Men bring Gifts and hom - age to our King!
With the an - gels let us sing Al - le - lu - ia to our King!

Rests in heav - en - ly peace, Rests in heav - en - ly peace.
Christ the Sav - iour is here! Je - sus the Sav - iour is here!"
Christ the Sav - iour is born, Je - sus the Sav - iour is born!
Christ the Sav - iour is born, Je - sus the Sav - iour is born!

O Little Town of Bethlehem

ST. LOUIS

Phillips Brooks, 1868

Lewis H. Redner, 1868

1. O lit-tle town of Beth-le-hem, How still we see thee lie;
2. For Christ is born of Ma-ry; And gath-ered all a-bove,
3. How si-lent-ly, how si-lent-ly The won-drous gift is given!
4. O ho-ly Child of Beth-le-hem, De-scend to us, we pray;

A-bove thy deep and dream-less sleep The si-lent stars go by.
While mor-tals sleep, the an-gels keep Their watch of won-dering love.
So God im-parts to hu-man hearts The bless-ings of His heaven.
Cast out our sin, and en-ter in, Be born in us to-day.

Yet in thy dark streets shin-eth The ev-er-last-ing Light;
O morn-ing stars, to-geth-er Pro-claim the ho-ly birth;
No ear may hear His com-ing, But in this world of sin,
We hear the Christ-mas an-gels The great glad ti-dings tell;

The hopes and fears of all the years Are met in thee to-night.
And prais-es sing to God the King, And peace to men on earth.
Where meek souls will re-ceive Him still, The dear Christ en-ters in.
O come to us, a-bide with us, Our Lord Em-man-u-el.

The First Noel

THE FIRST NOEL

Old English Carol

Traditional Melody in W. Sandys' "Christmas Carols," 1833

1. The first No - el the an - gels did say, Was to cer - tain poor
2. They look - ed up and they saw a star Shin - ing in the
3. And by the light of that same star, Three Wise Men
4. This star drew nigh to the north- west, O'er Beth - le - hem

shep-herds, in fields as they lay, In fields where they lay a - keep- ing their
East be - yond them far, And to the earth it gave great
came from a coun - try a - far, To seek for a king was their in -
then it took its rest, And there it did both stop and

REFRAIN

sheep, On a cold win -ter's night that was so deep. No - el, No -
light, And so it con - tin - ued both day and night.
tent, And to fol - low the star wher - ev - er it went.
stay, Right o - ver the place where Je - sus lay.

el, No - el, No - el, Born is the King of Is - ra - el!

The French word noël comes from the Latin natalis, "birthday." So Noel is used for Christmas, the birthday of Christ.

We Three Kings of Orient Are

KINGS OF ORIENT

John H. Hopkins, 1862   John H. Hopkins, 1862

1. We three kings of O - ri - ent are; Bear - ing gifts we trav-erse a - far
2. Born a king on Beth - le-hem's plain, Gold I bring to crown Him a - gain;
3. Frank - in - cense to of - fer have I; In - cense owns a de - i - ty nigh;
4. Myrrh is mine; its bit - ter per - fume Breathes a life of gath - er - ing gloom:
5. Glo - rious now be - hold Him a - rise, King and God and Sac - ri - fice;

Field and foun - tain, moor and moun-tain, Fol - low - ing yon - der star.
King for - ev - er, ceas - ing nev - er O - ver us all to reign.
Prayer and prais - ing all men rais - ing, Wor - ship Him, God on high.
Sor - rowing, sigh - ing, bleed - ing, dy - ing, Sealed in the stone - cold tomb.
Al - le - lu - ia, al - le - lu - ia! Earth to heaven re - plies.

REFRAIN

O star of won - der, star of night, Star with roy - al beau - ty bright,

West - ward lead - ing, still pro - ceed - ing, Guide us to thy per - fect Light.

A King Might Miss the Guiding Star

BETHLEHEM ROAD

Louis F. Benson, 1921

Calvin W. Laufer, 1925

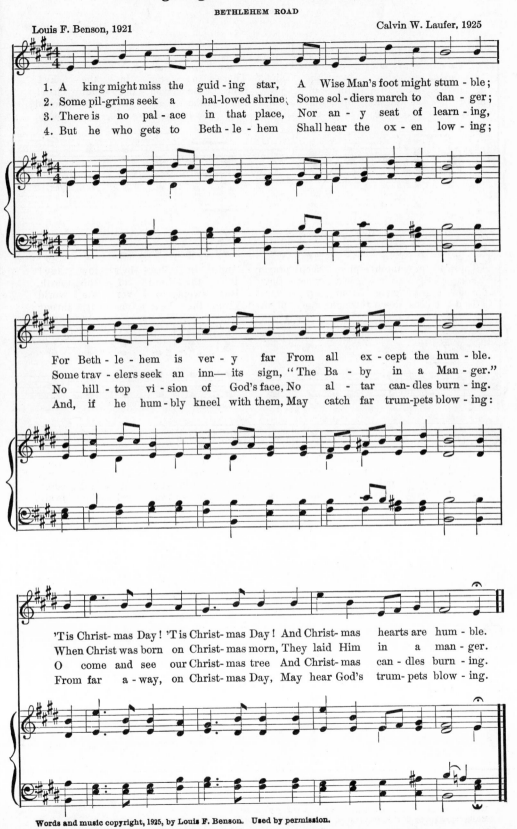

1. A king might miss the guid-ing star, A Wise Man's foot might stum-ble;
2. Some pil-grims seek a hal-lowed shrine, Some sol-diers march to dan-ger;
3. There is no pal-ace in that place, Nor an-y seat of learn-ing,
4. But he who gets to Beth-le-hem Shall hear the ox-en low-ing;

For Beth-le-hem is ver-y far From all ex-cept the hum-ble.
Some trav-elers seek an inn— its sign, "The Ba-by in a Man-ger."
No hill-top vi-sion of God's face, No al-tar can-dles burn-ing.
And, if he hum-bly kneel with them, May catch far trum-pets blow-ing:

'Tis Christ-mas Day! 'T is Christ-mas Day! And Christ-mas hearts are hum-ble.
When Christ was born on Christ-mas morn, They laid Him in a man-ger.
O come and see our Christ-mas tree And Christ-mas can-dles burn-ing.
From far a-way, on Christ-mas Day, May hear God's trum-pets blow-ing.

There's a Song in the Air

CHRISTMAS SONG

Josiah G. Holland, 1872

Karl P. Harrington, 1904

1. There's a song in the air! There's a star in the sky!
2. There's a tu - mult of joy O'er the won - der - ful birth!
3. In the light of that star Lie the a - ges im - pearled;
4. We re - joice in the light, And we ech - o the song

There's a moth - er's deep prayer And a ba - by's low cry!
For the Vir - gin's sweet Boy Is the Lord of the earth.
And that song from a - far Has swept o - ver the world.
That comes down through the night From the heav - en - ly throng;

And the star rains its fire while the beau - ti - ful sing,
Aye! the star rains its fire and the beau - ti - ful sing,
Ev - ery hearth is a - flame, and the beau - ti - ful sing
Aye! we shout to the love - ly e - van - gel they bring,

For the man - ger of Beth - le - hem cra - dles a King.
For the man - ger of Beth - le - hem cra - dles a King.
In the homes of the na - tions that Je - sus is King.
And we greet in His cra - dle our Sav - iour and King.

Fairest Lord Jesus

SCHÖNSTER HERR JESU

German, 17th century

Silesian Folk Song
From "Schlesische Volkslieder," Leipzig, 1842

1. Fair - est Lord Je - sus, Rul - er of all na - ture,
2. Fair are the mead - ows, Fair - er still the wood - lands,
3. Fair is the sun - shine, Fair - er still the moon - light,

O Thou of God and man the Son, Thee will I cher - ish,
Robed in the bloom - ing garb of spring: Je - sus is fair - er,
And all the twin - kling, star - ry host: Je - sus shines bright - er,

Thee will I hon - or, Thou, my soul's Glo - ry, Joy, and Crown.
Je - sus is pur - er, Who makes the woe - ful heart to sing.
Je - sus shines pur - er, Than all the an - gels heaven can boast.

42

Who Is the Child So Young and Fair?

JESU! REDEMPTOR OMNIUM

Martin Luther, 1535

Ancient Church Melody
From "Katholisches Kirchengesangbuch," 1625

1. Give heed, my heart, lift up thine eyes! What is it in that man-ger lies?
2. My heart for ver-y joy doth leap, My lips no more can si-lence keep;
3. Glo-ry to God in high-est heaven, Who un-to man His Son has given,

Who is the child so young and fair? The bless-ed Christ-child li-eth there.
I too must sing with joy-ful tongue That sweet-est, dear-est cra-dle song.
While an-gels sing, our hearts to cheer, To all the earth a glad new year!

43

I Heard the Bells on Christmas Day

TITSWORTH

Henry W. Longfellow, 1863

Lawrence Curry, 1928

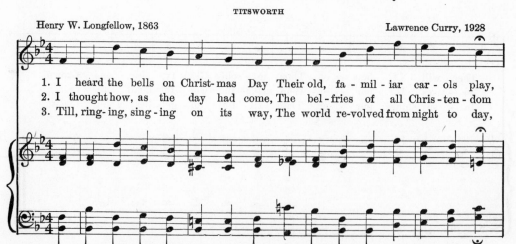

1. I heard the bells on Christ-mas Day Their old, fa-mil-iar car-ols play,
2. I thought how, as the day had come, The bel-fries of all Chris-ten-dom
3. Till, ring-ing, sing-ing on its way, The world re-volved from night to day,

I Heard the Bells on Christmas Day (concluded)

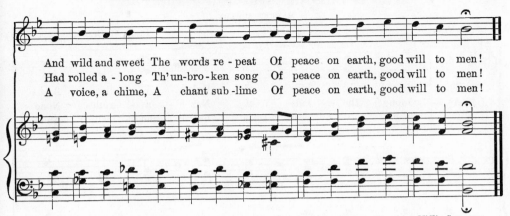

And wild and sweet The words re - peat Of peace on earth, good will to men!
Had rolled a - long Th'un-bro-ken song Of peace on earth, good will to men!
A   voice, a chime, A   chant sub -lime Of peace on earth, good will to men!

The Shepherds' Carol   44

THIS ENDRIS NIGHT

Iorwerth Llyfnwy, alt.

Old English Carol Tune
Harmonized by Lawrence Curry

1. The Lord of love came down to earth And was   a   ba - by born,
2. 'Twas but   a   low - ly man - ger bed Where In - fant Je - sus lay,
3. The low - ly shep - herds, poor - ly clad, Who came to   greet the Boy;
4. Let   us,   in love, with them u - nite, And with the an - gels sing

And an - gels sang with heaven - ly mirth On that fair Christ-mas morn.
No   oth - er place to lay His head Had God's dear Son that day.
When Him they saw, their hearts were glad And leaped with love and joy.
The birth - day of the world's De - light, Our glo - rious Sav - iour King.

45 Among the Lads of Nazareth

MARKET SQUARE

F. M. B.

Frank M. Braselman, 1926

1. The friend-ly hills of Gal - i - lee, A-
2. A - mong the lads of Naz - a - reth None
3. In ear - ly years He heard the call, And

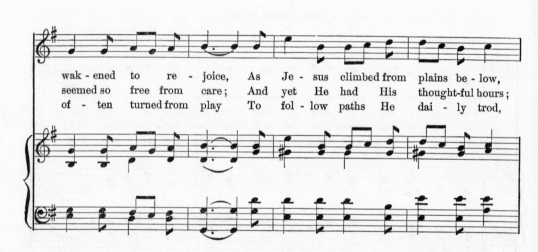

wak - ened to re - joice, As Je - sus climbed from plains be - low,
seemed so free from care; And yet He had His thought-ful hours;
of - ten turned from play To fol - low paths He dai - ly trod,

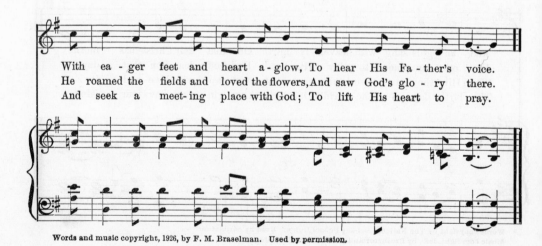

With ea - ger feet and heart a - glow, To hear His Fa - ther's voice.
He roamed the fields and loved the flowers, And saw God's glo - ry there.
And seek a meet-ing place with God; To lift His heart to pray.

At Work Beside His Father's Bench

IHR HIRTEN, STEHET ALLE AUF

A Carol Tune from the Tyrol, c. 1610
Harmonized by Lawrence Curry

Alice M. Pullen; alt.

With vigor

1. At work be-side His fa-ther's bench, At play when work was done;
In qui-et Gal-i-lee He lived—The Friend of ev-ery-one.
And in the lit-tle flat-roofed house He served with will-ing hand;
His moth-er's dai-ly bur-dens bore, Her joys and pleas-ures planned.

2. And as He grew to be a man He wan-dered far and wide,
To be a Friend to ev-ery-one Through-out the coun-try-side.
Through hard-ships and through dan-gers too, Un-daunt-ed, tire-less, brave;
For trou-bled, sick, and wea-ry friends His dai-ly life He gave.

3. And when He left His faith-ful friends To do His work and will,
He prom-ised them He'd be, un-seen, Their faith-ful Com-rade still.
Com-rade of boys and girls like us, Play-mate so straight and true,
In all our work, in all our play, Make us true com-rades too.

Tell Me the Stories of Jesus

STORIES OF JESUS

W. H. Parker, 1904

F. A. Challinor, 1904

1. Tell me the sto-ries of Je-sus I love to hear;
2. First let me hear how the chil-dren Stood round His knee;
3. In-to the cit-y I'd fol-low The chil-dren's band,
4. Tell me, in ac-cents of won-der, How rolled the sea,

Things I would ask Him to tell me If He were here; Scenes by the way-side,
And I shall fan-cy His bless-ing Rest-ing on me; Words full of kind-ness,
Wav-ing a branch of a palm tree High in my hand; One of His her-alds,
Toss-ing the boat in a tem-pest On Gal-i-lee! And how the Mas-ter,

Tales of the sea, Sto-ries of Je-sus, Tell them to me.
Deeds full of grace, All in the love light Of Je-sus' face.
Yes, I would sing Loud-est ho-san-nas! Je-sus is King!
Read-y and kind, Chid-ed the bil-lows, And hushed the wind.

To Thee, Redeemer, King

48

ST. THEODULPH

Theodulph of Orleans, c. 820
Trans. by John M. Neale, 1854; alt.

Melchior Teschner, c. 1615

1. All glo - ry, laud, and hon - or To Thee, Re - deem - er, King,
2. Thou art the King of Is - ra - el, Thou Da - vid's roy - al Son,
3. Thou didst ac - cept their prais - es; Ac - cept the prayers we bring,

To whom the lips of chil - dren Made sweet ho - san - nas ring.
Who in the Lord's Name com - est, The King and bless - ed One.
Who in all good de - light - est, Thou good and gra - cious King.

The peo - ple of the He - brews With palms be - fore Thee went;
To Thee, be - fore Thy Pas - sion, They sang their hymns of praise;
All glo - ry, laud, and hon - or To Thee, Re - deem - er, King,

Our praise and prayer and an - thems Be - fore Thee we pre - sent.
To Thee, now high ex - alt - ed, Our mel - o - dy we raise.
To whom the lips of chil - dren Made sweet ho - san - nas ring.

49 Thy Works of Love

DUNDEE (FRENCH)

Calvin W. Laufer, 1926

"Scottish Psalter," 1615

1. Thy works of love and friend-ship, Lord, Help us to think of Thee;
2. They bring to mind the qui - et scene When chil - dren climbed Thy knee,
3. And once the crowd, so wea - ry, sad, Surged round Thee like a tide,
4. In vil - lage, mar - ket place, and throng, The chil - dren cheered Thy days;
5. We love Thee for Thy works di - vine, Still more for what Thou art;

Thy heal - ing won - ders and Thy word Re - call fair Gal - i - lee.
And when Thou saidst with friend - ly mien, "Let them come un - to me."
Yet Thy great heart sought out a lad And drew him to Thy side.
And in the Tem - ple court their song To Thee was per - fect praise.
And that our lives may be like Thine, We give Thee, Lord, our heart.

50 There Is a Green Hill Far Away

MEDITATION

Cecil Frances Alexander, 1848

John H. Gower, 1890

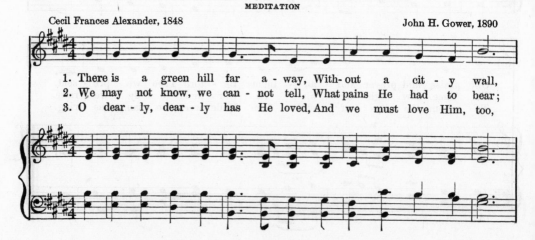

1. There is a green hill far a - way, With-out a cit - y wall,
2. We may not know, we can - not tell, What pains He had to bear;
3. O dear - ly, dear - ly has He loved, And we must love Him, too,

There Is a Green Hill Far Away (concluded)

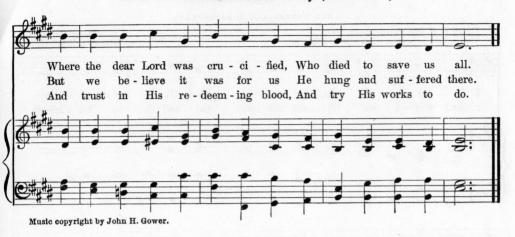

Where the dear Lord was cru - ci - fied, Who died to save us all.
But we be - lieve it was for us He hung and suf - fered there.
And trust in His re - deem - ing blood, And try His works to do.

Music copyright by John H. Gower.

In the Cross of Christ I Glory   51

RATHBUN

John Bowring, 1825   Ithamar Conkey, 1851

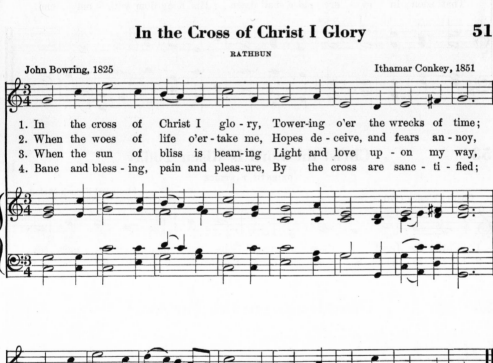

1. In the cross of Christ I glo - ry, Tower - ing o'er the wrecks of time;
2. When the woes of life o'er - take me, Hopes de - ceive, and fears an - noy,
3. When the sun of bliss is beam - ing Light and love up - on my way,
4. Bane and bless - ing, pain and pleas - ure, By the cross are sanc - ti - fied;

All the light of sa - cred sto - ry Gath - ers round its head sub - lime.
Nev - er shall the cross for - sake me: Lo! it glows with peace and joy.
From the cross the ra - diance stream - ing Adds more lus - ter to the day.
Peace is there that knows no meas - ure, Joys that through all time a - bide.

He Is Risen

NUN DANKET ALL' (GRÄFENBERG)

Georg F. P. von Hardenberg, 1802
Trans. by Catherine Winkworth, 1858; alt.

Johann Crüger's
"Praxis Pietatis Melica," 1653

1. I say to all men, far and near, That He is risen to - day;
2. And what I say, let each this morn Go tell it to his friend,

That He is with us now and here, And ev - er - more shall stay.
That soon in ev - ery place shall dawn His King-dom with - out end.

53 ## Christ the Lord Is Risen Today

ORIENTIS PARTIBUS

Charles Wesley (1707–1788)

Medieval French Melody
Attributed to Pierre de Corbeil

1. "Christ the Lord is risen to - day," Sons of men and an - gels say;
2. Love's re - deem - ing work is done, Fought the fight, the bat - tle won;

Raise your joys and tri - umphs high; Sing, ye heavens, and earth, re - ply.
Death in vain for - bids Him rise; Christ has o - pened Par - a - dise.

Jesus Christ Is Risen Today

EASTER HYMN

From the Latin, 14th century
Stanza 3, Charles Wesley, 1740

"Lyra Davidica," 1708

1. Je - sus Christ is risen to - day, Al - le - lu - ia!
2. Hymns of praise then let us sing Al - le - lu - ia!
3. Sing we to our God a - bove Al - le - lu - ia!

Our tri - um - phant ho - ly day, Al - le - lu - ia!
Un - to Christ, our heaven - ly King, Al - le - lu - ia!
Praise e - ter - nal as His love; Al - le - lu - ia!

Who did once, up - on the cross, Al - le - lu - ia!
Who en - dured the cross and grave, Al - le - lu - ia!
Praise Him, all ye heaven - ly host, Al - le - lu - ia!

Suf - fer to re - deem our loss. Al - le - lu - ia!
Sin - ners to re - deem and save. Al - le - lu - ia!
Fa - ther, Son, and Ho - ly Ghost. Al - le - lu - ia!

The Strife Is O'er, the Battle Done

PALESTRINA

Anon. (Latin)
Trans. by Francis Pott, 1861

Arr. from Giovanni P. da Palestrina, 1591

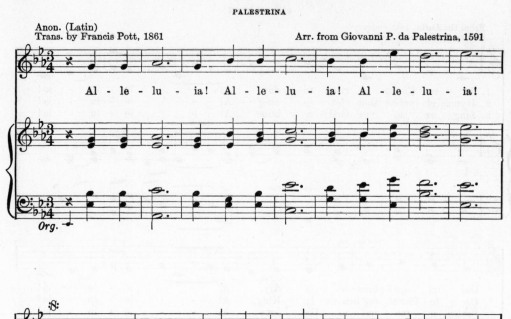

Al - le - lu - ia! Al - le - lu - ia! Al - le - lu - ia!

Org.

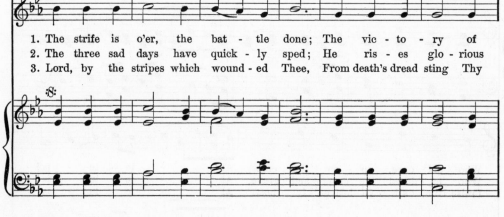

1. The strife is o'er, the bat - tle done; The vic - to - ry of
2. The three sad days have quick - ly sped; He ris - es glo - rious
3. Lord, by the stripes which wound - ed Thee, From death's dread sting Thy

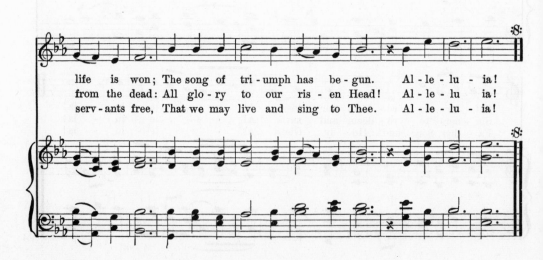

life is won; The song of tri - umph has be - gun. Al - le - lu - ia!
from the dead: All glo - ry to our ris - en Head! Al - le - lu - ia!
serv - ants free, That we may live and sing to Thee. Al - le - lu - ia!

O Joyous Easter Morning

MEIRIONYDD

Welsh Hymn Melody

O joy - ous Eas - ter morn - ing That saw the Lord a - rise!

O bright and hap - py morn - ing! The clouds have left the skies.

O glad - some Eas - ter morn - ing! Christ is the Vic - tor King!

Then let us all with glad - ness Our thank - ful prais - es sing.

Christ Triumphant

AUSTRIAN HYMN

Miriam Drury, 1936

Franz Joseph Haydn, 1797

1. Christ the King rides forth in tri - umph. "Hail!" the host their prais - es sing;
2. Lo, He comes a - gain tri - um - phant, Chris - tian peo - ple, loud - ly sing;

Youth and age with glad ho - san - nas Hail with joy their na - tion's King;
Thou - sand thou - sands bow be - fore Him, Loud ac - claim - ing Christ their King;

"Hail!" the throng re - peats the cho - rus, Cast - ing gar - ments in His way,
King of na - tions far and scat - tered, West and East to dis - tant shore,

Palms of vic - to - ry they wave on high As He rides the streets to - day.
King of peace and King of love, King of life for - ev - er - more.

Consecration

SEYMOUR

Frances R. Havergal, 1874

Arr. from Carl M. von Weber, 1826

1. Take my life, and let it be Con - se - crat - ed, Lord, to Thee.
2. Take my hands, and let them move At the im - pulse of Thy love.
3. Take my voice, and let me sing, Al - ways, on - ly, for my King.
4. Take my love; my Lord, I pour At Thy feet its treas - ure store.

Take my mo-ments and my days; Let them flow in cease-less praise.
Take my feet, and let them be Swift and beau - ti - ful for Thee.
Take my lips, and let them be Filled with mes - sa - ges from Thee.
Take my - self, and I will be Ev - er, on - ly, all for Thee. A - MEN.

Friend of the Young

JUST AS I AM

Marianne Hearn Farningham, 1887

Joseph Barnby, 1893

1. Just as I am, Thine own to be, Friend of the young, who lov - est me,
2. I would live ev - er in the light; I would work ev - er for the right;
3. Just as I am, young, strong, and free, To be the best that I can be

To con - se - crate my - self to Thee, O Je - sus Christ, I come.
I would serve Thee with all my might; There - fore, to Thee I come.
For truth, and right-eous-ness, and Thee, Lord of my life, I come. A - MEN.

60 # Dear Lord, We Give Our Youth to Thee

GREEN HILL

Calvin W. Laufer, 1926

Albert L. Peace, 1885

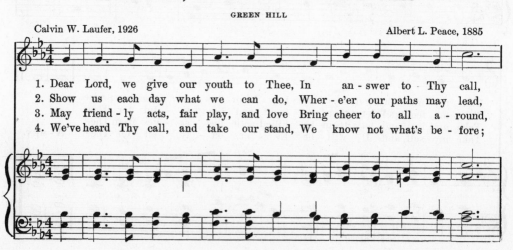

1. Dear Lord, we give our youth to Thee, In an - swer to Thy call,
2. Show us each day what we can do, Wher - e'er our paths may lead,
3. May friend - ly acts, fair play, and love Bring cheer to all a - round,
4. We've heard Thy call, and take our stand, We know not what's be - fore;

Dear Lord, We Give Our Youth to Thee (concluded)

And pray our hearts may loy - al be To love Thee best of all.
To dare the right, to seek the true, To com - fort those in need.
That this fair earth, like heaven a - bove, May with Thy peace a - bound.
But we are Thine with heart and hand, To serve Thee ev - er - more. A - MEN.

Following Christ   61

HORSHAM

Josephine L. Baldwin   English Traditional Melody

1. Sav - iour, in the words I say May I fol - low Thine own way;
2. Show me how to play each game Fair and square, as in Thy Name;
3. In my home, at play, at school, May I keep the Gold - en Rule;

And in all the deeds I do Show a spir - it fair and true.
Lose the con - test if I must, But in ev - ery act be just.
Brave - ly face the hard - est test, Love my neigh - bors, do my best. A - MEN.

I Would Be True

PEEK

Howard Arnold Walter (1883–1918)　　　　　　　　　　　　　　Joseph Yates Peek

1. I would be true, for there are those who trust me; I would be
2. I would be friend of all—the foe, the friend-less; I would be

pure, for there are those who care; I would be strong, for
giv - ing, and for - get the gift; I would be hum - ble,

there is much to suf - fer; I would be brave, for there is much to
for I know my weak - ness; I would look up, and laugh, and love, and

dare, 　　I would be brave, for there is much to dare.
lift, 　　I would look up, and laugh, and love, and lift.

D'ARCY

Doris M. Gill, 1938

Lawrence Curry, 1939

With vigor

1. Best of all the things we do— Jump - ing, chas - ing, throw - ing,
2. Who but Thee could shape a man, Sup - ple, swift, and dar - ing?
3. Riv - ers ra - cing full and free, Sea - ward now are go - ing:

Skip - ping, bath - ing, rid - ing, sail - ing— Best of all is grow - ing.
Shed through ev - ery vein and mus - cle En - er - gy un - spar - ing?
So the joy and vig - or in us Back to Thee are flow - ing.

Some -thing calls us on - ward, up - ward; Might- y Mak - er, is it Thou?
Thou who mad - est flame and snow- flake, Spi - der's web and new- born foal,
Take our brim-ming strength and use it; Let our minds be nim - ble, free;

Is Thy strength with-in us ris - ing Like the life with - in the bough?
Made these eyes for our de - light - ing, Made the mind we each con - trol.
Keep our spir - its ev - er reach - ing Up - ward, God of Truth, to Thee.

Dare to Be True

DARE TO BE BRAVE

W. J. Rooper; alt.

Duncan Hume

1. Dare to be brave, dare to be true; Strive for the right, for the Lord is with you; Fight with sin brave - ly, fight and be strong; Christ is your Cap - tain; fear on - ly what's wrong.
2. Dare to be brave, dare to be true; God is your Fa - ther: He watch - es o'er you; He knows your tri - als; when your heart quails, Ask Him to help you; His grace nev - er fails.
3. Dare to be brave, dare to be true; God grant you cour - age to car - ry you through; Try to help oth - ers; ev - er be kind; Let all the err - ing a friend in you find.

REFRAIN

Fight then, good sol - diers, fight and be brave; Christ is your Cap - tain, might - y to save.

Let Us Be Loyal

VIRTUS

Nancy Byrd Turner

Emily S. Perkins

Let us be loy - al! Heart and hand Pledged to our home, and our friends, our land;

Pledged to our work, that day by day It shall be done in a faith - ful way;

Pledged to be kind, pledged to be true, Pledged to be brave our whole lives through;

Read - y to do our best we stand And give our loy - al heart and hand.

66   We Would Bring Our Treasures

LAUFER

Anon.

Emily S. Perkins, 1924

1. The wise may bring their learn - ing; The rich may bring their wealth;
2. We'll bring the lit - tle du - ties We have to do each day;

And some may bring their great - ness; And some bring strength and health;
We'll try our best to please Him, At home, at school, at play:

We too would bring our treas - ures To of - fer to the King;
And bet - ter are these treas - ures To of - fer to our King

We have no wealth or learn - ing: What shall we chil - dren bring?
Than rich - est gifts with - out them; Yet these we all may bring.

For Man's Unceasing Quest for God

COTTINGHAM

Alice M. Pullen

Air by Alice M. Pullen
Harmonized by Hilda M. Dodd

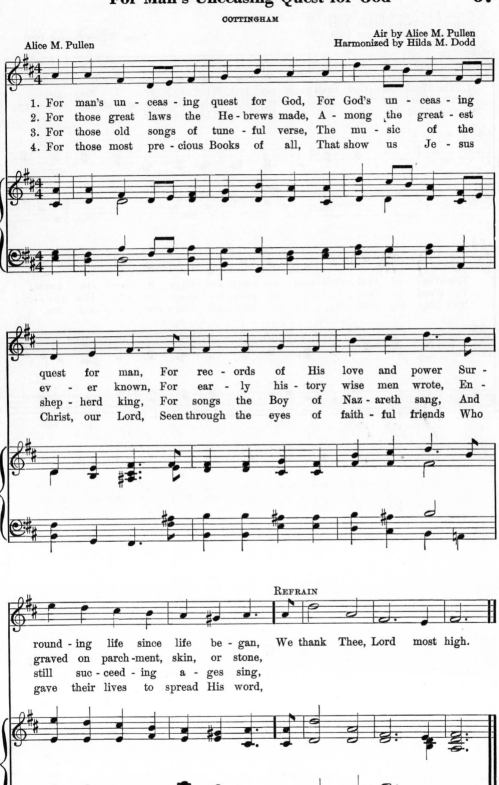

1. For man's un - ceas - ing quest for God, For God's un - ceas - ing
2. For those great laws the He - brews made, A - mong the great - est
3. For those old songs of tune - ful verse, The mu - sic of the
4. For those most pre - cious Books of all, That show us Je - sus

quest for man, For rec - ords of His love and power Sur -
ev - er known, For ear - ly his - tory wise men wrote, En -
shep - herd king, For songs the Boy of Naz - areth sang, And
Christ, our Lord, Seen through the eyes of faith - ful friends Who

REFRAIN

round - ing life since life be - gan, We thank Thee, Lord most high.
graved on parch - ment, skin, or stone,
still suc - ceed - ing a - ges sing,
gave their lives to spread His word,

68   **The Word of God**

Stanza 1 by Nancy Byrd Turner, 1926
Stanza 2 by Vivien Brown, 1939
Stanza 3 by Ruth Manner, 1939

Grace Wilbur Conant, 1926

With spirit

1. The Word of God shall guide my feet, Wher-ev-er I may go;
2. The Word of God up-on my lips Helps me to spread the sto-ry;
3. Our God is with us all the time, Wher-ev-er we may be;

The Word of God shall teach my heart The things it ought to know;
The Word of God be-fore my eyes Will show me all His glo-ry;
He's help-ing, guid-ing, lov-ing All chil-dren, e-ven me.

The Word of God shall make me strong And bless me through my
The Word of God with-in my heart Will give me strength to
I'll read His Word and keep His law And love Him dai-ly

whole life long, And bless me through my whole life long.
do my part, Will give me strength to do my part.
more and more, And love Him dai-ly more and more.

Lord, Thy Word Abideth

Henry W. Baker, 1861

Richard R. Chope, 1862

Lord, Thy Word a - bid - eth, And our foot - steps guid - eth;

Who its truth be - liev - eth Light and joy re - ceiv - eth.

My Guide

BEATITUDO

70

Calvin W. Laufer, 1926

John B. Dykes, 1875

1. The Word of God shall be my guide And teach me ev - ery day;
2. There is a Life for me to live, And God would be there - in,

Its truth will keep me near His side And help me go His way.
That by His pres - ence He may give The power to strive and win.

Words copyright, 1927, by Calvin W. Laufer. Used by permission.

71 The Lord's My Shepherd

PASTOR MEUS

Psalm 23
"Scottish Psalter," 1650

Lawrence Curry, 1939

1. The Lord's my Shep-herd, I'll not want; He makes me down to lie
2. My soul He doth re-store a-gain; And me to walk doth make
3. Yea, though I walk in death's dark vale, Yet will I fear none ill;
4. My ta-ble Thou hast fur-nish-ed In pres-ence of my foes;
5. Good-ness and mer-cy all my life Shall sure-ly fol-low me;

In pas-tures green; He lead-eth me The qui-et wa-ters by.
With-in the paths of right-eous-ness, E'en for His own Name's sake.
For Thou art with me; and Thy rod And staff me com-fort still.
My head Thou dost with oil a-noint, And my cup o-ver-flows.
And in God's house for-ev-er-more My dwell-ing place shall be.

Music copyright, 1940, by Presbyterian Board of Christian Education.

72 My Father's Care

EUDORA

Stanza 1 anon.
Stanza 2 by Blanche Hoke

J. R. Murray

1. How strong and sweet my Fa-ther's care, That round a-bout me, like the air,
2. O Fa-ther, help me, then, each day To fol-low al-ways Thy good Way,

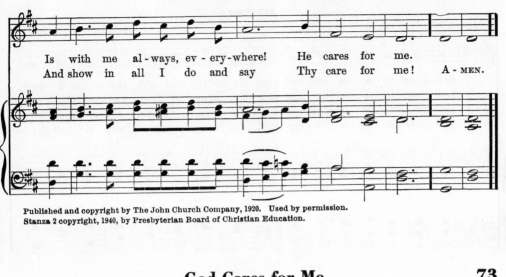

Is with me al-ways, ev-ery-where! He cares for me.
And show in all I do and say Thy care for me! A-MEN.

God Cares for Me 73

BEECHWOOD

Sarah B. Rhodes   Josiah Booth

1. God, who made the earth, The air, the sky, the sea,
2. God, who made the grass, The flower, the fruit, the tree,
3. God, who made the sun, The moon, the stars, is He
4. God, who made all things On earth, in air, in sea,

Who gave the light its birth, Car-eth for me.
The day and night to pass, Car-eth for me.
Who, when life's clouds come on, Car-eth for me.
Who chan-ging sea-sons brings, Car-eth for me.

God Speaks to Us

ELMHURST

Joseph Johnson, 1890; alt.

Edwin D. Drewett, 1887

1. God speaks to us in bird and song, In winds that drift the clouds a - long,
2. God speaks to us in far and near, In peace of home and friends most dear,
3. God speaks to us in dark-est night, By qui - et ways through morn-ings bright,
4. God speaks to us in ev - ery land, On wave-lapped shore and si - lent strand,

A - bove the din of toil and wrong, A mel - o - dy of love.
From the dim past and pres - ent clear, A mel - o - dy of love.
When shad - ows fall with eve - ning light, A mel - o - dy of love.
Through kind - ly word and clasp of hand, A mel - o - dy of love.

75

The Lord Is Ever Near

ST. MICHAEL (OLD 134TH)

Anon.

Adapted from "Genevan Psalter," 1551

1. The Lord is ev - er near, He bids His chil - dren pray;
2. Our Fa - ther's love is sure, And ver - y wise His care;

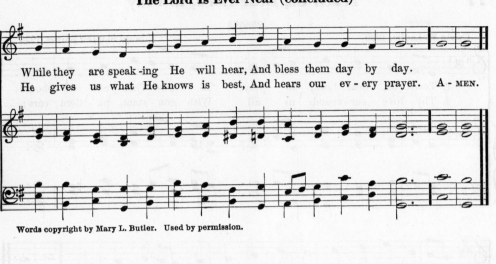

While they are speak-ing He will hear, And bless them day by day.
He gives us what He knows is best, And hears our ev-ery prayer. A - MEN.

God's Presence   76

DALEHURST

Calvin W. Laufer, 1926   Arthur Cottman, 1874

1. Like Thee, dear Mas - ter, help us feel That we are ne'er a - lone,
2. He walks un - seen be - side us all, The Friend who knows life's way;
3. Some-times He speaks to let us know That He is ver - y near;
4. O it is ver - y won - der - ful That in the world so fair

But have a Com - rade, tried and true, Who loves us as His own.
He stoops to note the sim - plest need And helps us, lest we stray.
Then all the nois - es of the world Are still that we may hear.
God's pres-ence moves in ev - ery-thing To help us do and dare!

77

Teach Us, Dear Lord, to Pray

GREENE

Calvin W. Laufer, 1926

Edward Shippen Barnes, 1926

1. Teach us, dear Lord, to pray, To trust Thee as we should;
2. Thy love sur-rounds us all With con-stant, pa-tient care;

And help us feel that, come what may, Thy gifts are al-ways good.
Thy ten-der heart, be-fore we call, A-waits our ear-nest prayer. A-MEN.

78

He Prayeth Best Who Loveth Best

ST. FLAVIAN

Samuel T. Coleridge, 1798

Adapted from "Day's Psalter," 1563

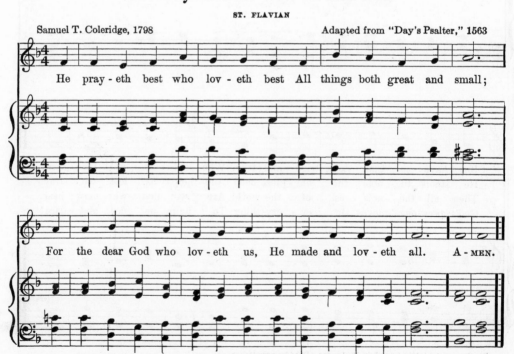

He pray-eth best who lov-eth best All things both great and small;

For the dear God who lov-eth us, He made and lov-eth all. A-MEN.

O Master Workman of the Race

79

AMESBURY

Jay T. Stocking, 1912

Uzziah C. Burnap, 1895

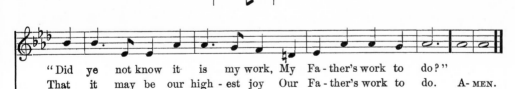

1. O Mas - ter Work - man of the race, Thou Man of Gal - i - lee,
2. O Thou who dost the vi - sion send And giv - est each his task,

Who with the eyes of ear - ly youth E - ter - nal things didst see,
And with the task suf - fi - cient strength, Show us Thy will, we ask;

We thank Thee for Thy boy - hood faith That shone Thy whole life through;
Give us a con - science bold and good, Give us a pur - pose true,

"Did ye not know it is my work, My Fa - ther's work to do?"
That it may be our high - est joy Our Fa - ther's work to do. A- MEN.

80
Show Me What I Ought to Do

ST. BEES

John P. Hopps, 1877; alt.

John B. Dykes, 1862

1. Fa - ther, lead me day by day, Ev - er in Thine own good* way;
2. When in dan - ger, make me brave, Make me know that Thou canst save;
3. When I'm tempt - ed to do wrong, Make me stead - fast, wise, and strong;

Teach me to be kind** and true; Show me what I ought to do.
Keep me safe by Thy dear side; Let me in Thy love a - bide.
And when all a - lone I stand, Shield me with Thy might - y hand. A-MEN.

Words copyright by The National Sunday School Union. Used by permission.
* "Sweet" in original.
** "Pure" in original.

81
I Thank You, God

CE JOUR

Frances McKinnon Morton

French Traditional Melody

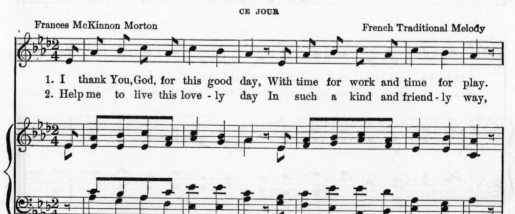

1. I thank You, God, for this good day, With time for work and time for play.
2. Help me to live this love - ly day In such a kind and friend - ly way,

I Thank You, God (concluded)

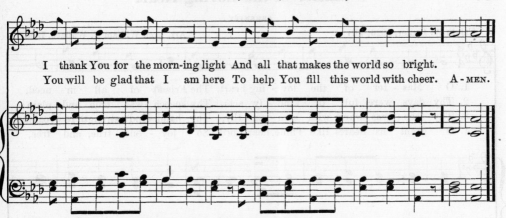

I thank You for the morn-ing light And all that makes the world so bright.

You will be glad that I am here To help You fill this world with cheer. A - MEN.

Growing like Jesus

82

TROUT

Ethel Wendell Trout, 1926; alt.   Calvin W. Laufer, 1926; alt.

1. O   Je - sus, Lad   of   Naz - a - reth, Help   us   this   day   to   grow
2. Thou wast   o - be - dient, hap - py, true, Though with a   spir - it   free,
3. O   Je - sus, Lad   of   Naz - a - reth, Help   us   this   day   to   grow
4. Help us   to   live   as Thou didst live, And   in   our homes to   be

In   fa - vor with both God and man, As Thou didst, long   a - go.
There in   Thy lov - ing, hum - ble home, O Lad   of   Gal - i - lee!
In   wis - dom and in   stat - ure too, As Thou didst, long   a - go.
O - be - dient, hap - py, kind, and true, O Lad   of   Gal - i - lee!   A - MEN.

83 O Master of the Loving Heart

SERENITY

Calvin W. Laufer, 1926; alt.

Arr. from William V. Wallace, 1856

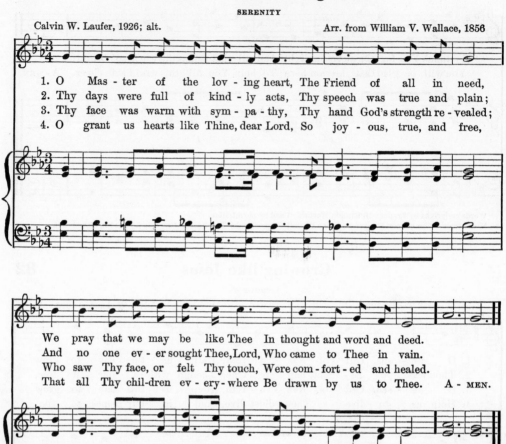

1. O Mas-ter of the lov-ing heart, The Friend of all in need,
2. Thy days were full of kind-ly acts, Thy speech was true and plain;
3. Thy face was warm with sym-pa-thy, Thy hand God's strength re-vealed;
4. O grant us hearts like Thine, dear Lord, So joy-ous, true, and free,

We pray that we may be like Thee In thought and word and deed.
And no one ev-er sought Thee, Lord, Who came to Thee in vain.
Who saw Thy face, or felt Thy touch, Were com-fort-ed and healed.
That all Thy chil-dren ev-ery-where Be drawn by us to Thee. A-MEN.

84 Building

Barbara M. Hobbs; alt.

Barbara M. Hobbs

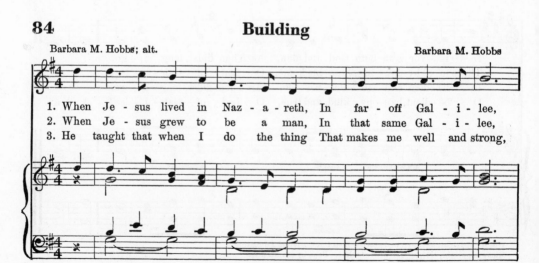

1. When Je-sus lived in Naz-a-reth, In far-off Gal-i-lee,
2. When Je-sus grew to be a man, In that same Gal-i-lee,
3. He taught that when I do the thing That makes me well and strong,

Building (concluded)

And Jo - seph was a car - pen - ter, Who build - ed joy - ful - ly;
The peo - ple heard him glad - ly as He taught be - side the sea.
That when I choose the bet - ter things, Re - fus - ing what is wrong,

I think that Je - sus watched him as He ham-mered strong and true;
He said that we are car - pen - ters, But in a dif - ferent way;
That when I do the help - ful things, The things I know I should,

And helped him in the work- shop with The things a boy could do.
We build a life of use - ful - ness Through what we do or say.
My life will be a use - ful one, And God will call it good.

85 Always My Friend

FRÉOND

Wilhelmina D'A. Stephens, 1939

Lawrence Curry, 1939

With vigor

1. Je - sus, Christ Je - sus, is with me to - day: Lov - ing me,
2. Je - sus, Christ Je - sus, is al - ways my Friend; His love and
3. Je - sus, Christ Je - sus, I want to thank Thee: Thy loy - al

guid - ing me, when I'm at play; Help - ing me, teach - ing me,
pa - tience have nev - er an end. When I'm in trou - ble, to
help - er may I al - ways be, Fol - low - ing Thee in my

when I'm at work, Keep - ing me hap - py, not let - ting me shirk.
Him I can go; He's nev - er failed me—He'll help me, I know.
liv - ing each day, Shar - ing with oth - ers the joy of Thy way.

I Want to Be a Christian

Negro Spiritual
Harmonized by Lawrence Curry

1. Lord, I want to be a Chris-tian in-a my heart, in-a my
2. Lord, I want to be more lov-ing in-a my heart, in-a my
3. Lord, I want to be like Je-sus in-a my heart, in-a my

heart; Lord, I want to be a Chris-tian in-a my heart.
heart; Lord, I want to be more lov-ing in-a my heart.
heart; Lord, I want to be like Je-sus in-a my heart.

REFRAIN

In-a my heart, In-a my heart,

Lord, I want to be a Chris-tian in-a my heart.
Lord, I want to be more lov-ing in-a my heart.
Lord, I want to be like Je-sus in-a my heart.

Steal Away to Jesus

Negro Spiritual
Harmonized by Lawrence Curry

Steal a - way, steal a - way, steal a - way to Je - sus;

Steal a - way, steal a - way home, I ain't got long to stay here.

1. My Lord calls me, He calls me by the thun - der; The
2. My Lord calls me, He calls me by the light - ning; The

trum - pet sounds with - in - a my soul! I ain't got long to stay here.

Into All the World

Go, Ye Who Bear the Word!

MISSIONER

Nancy Byrd Turner, 1926

Grace Wilbur Conant, 1926

With vigor

1. The Word of God must go To wait - ing lands a - far,
2. The flag of God, un - furled, A - bove all storms shall toss
3. Go, ye who bear the Word! We'll pray, and strive, and give,

Till ev - ery dis - tant shore shall know The beau - ty of the star.
Un - til it sig - nals down the world The mean - ing of the cross.
Till hearts that love had nev - er stirred Shall see the Light, and live.

89 Brothers of the Faith

ST. PETER

John Oxenham, 1908

Alexander R. Reinagle, 1836

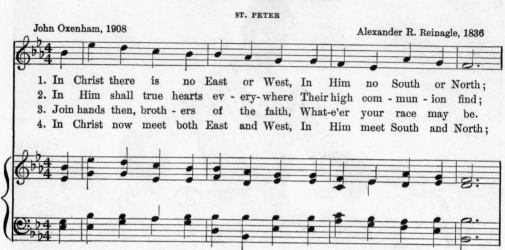

1. In Christ there is no East or West, In Him no South or North;
2. In Him shall true hearts ev - ery-where Their high com - mun - ion find;
3. Join hands then, broth - ers of the faith, What-e'er your race may be.
4. In Christ now meet both East and West, In Him meet South and North;

But one great fel - low - ship of love Through-out the whole wide earth.
His serv - ice is the gold - en cord Close bind - ing all man - kind.
Who serves my Fa - ther as a son Is sure - ly kin to me.
All Christ - ly souls are one in Him Through-out the whole wide earth.

Words from "Bees in Amber." Copyright by the American Tract Society. Used by permission.

90 We've a Story to Tell to the Nations

MESSAGE

Colin Sterne, 1896

H. Ernest Nichol, 1896

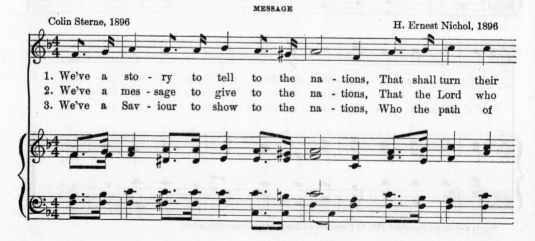

1. We've a sto - ry to tell to the na - tions, That shall turn their
2. We've a mes - sage to give to the na - tions, That the Lord who
3. We've a Sav - iour to show to the na - tions, Who the path of

We've a Story to Tell to the Nations (concluded)

hearts to the right, A sto - ry of truth and mer - cy,
reign - eth a - bove Hath sent us His Son to save us,
sor - row has trod, That all of the world's great peo - ples

A sto - ry of peace and light, A sto - ry of peace and light.
And show us that God is Love, And show us that God is Love.
Might come to the truth of God, Might come to the truth of God.

Refrain

For the dark - ness shall turn to dawn - ing, And the dawn - ing to noon-day bright,

And Christ's great King - dom shall come on earth, The King-dom of love and light.

91 Jesus Shall Reign

DUKE STREET

Psalm 72
Isaac Watts, 1719; alt.

John Hatton, c. 1793

1. Je - sus shall reign wher - e'er the sun Does his suc -
ces - sive jour - neys run; His King - dom stretch from
shore to shore, Till moons shall wax and wane no more.

2. For Him shall end - less prayer be made, And prais - es
throng to crown His head; His Name, like sweet per -
fume, shall rise With ev - ery morn - ing sac - ri - fice.

3. Peo - ple and realms of ev - ery tongue Dwell on His
love with sweet - est song; And chil - dren's voi - ces
shall pro - claim Their ear - ly bless - ings on His Name.

Our Church

TRURO

Mabel Niedermeyer, 1939

T. Williams' "Psalmodia Evangelica," 1789

1. Our church pro-claims God's love and care To all who work and wor-ship there, Who sing to-geth-er hymns of praise, And prayers of glad thanks-giv-ing raise.

2. Her hands reach out in serv-ice through Kind, help-ful deeds that Chris-tians do To show God's chil-dren of ev-ery land The world of love that He has planned.

3. Glad-ly we come our praise to sing, And gifts of friend-ly serv-ice bring; We too would know God's love and care, And work and joy with oth-ers share.

Words copyright, 1940, by Presbyterian Board of Christian Education.
Alternative tune, "Duke Street," number 91.

93 His Own Church

AUSTRIAN HYMN

Wilhelmina D'A. Stephens, 1939

Franz Joseph Haydn, 1797

1. Long a-go the friends of Je-sus Who had lived with Him each day
2. We would al-so strive to please Him, In His fel-low-ship would live;

Met to-geth-er for His wor-ship; Oth-ers fol-lowed in their way:
So we band our-selves to-geth-er, All our lives to Him to give:

Bound to-geth-er in one bod-y, Je-sus' friends the whole world o'er—
Tell-ing oth-ers of His good-ness, Win-ning them to love Him too—

His own Church, on His word found-ed, Him to hon-or ev-er-more.
His own Church, through all the a-ges, In the world His work to do.

Faith of Our Fathers

ST. CATHERINE

Frederick W. Faber, 1849
Stanzas 2, 3 alt.

Henry F. Hemy, 1865
Alt. by James G. Walton, 1871

1. Faith of our fa - thers! liv - ing still In spite of dun - geon,
2. Our fa - thers, chained in pris - ons dark, Were still in heart and
3. Faith of our fa - thers! God's great power Shall win all na - tions
4. Faith of our fa - thers! we will love Both friend and foe in

fire, and sword, O how our hearts beat high with joy
con - science free; And blest would be their chil - dren's fate
un - to thee; And through the truth that comes from God
all our strife, And preach thee, too, as love knows how

When-e'er we hear that glo - rious word: Faith of our fa - thers,
If they, like them, should die for thee: Faith of our fa - thers,
Man - kind shall then be tru - ly free: Faith of our fa - thers,
By kind - ly words and vir - tuous life: Faith of our fa - thers,

ho - ly faith! We will be true to thee till death.

Forward Through the Ages

HOWARD

Frederick L. Hosmer, 1908

Alonzo P. Howard (1838–1902)

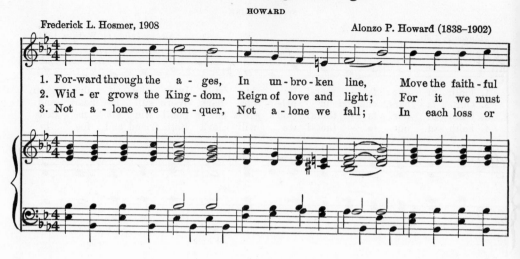

1. For-ward through the a - ges, In un-bro-ken line, Move the faith-ful
2. Wid - er grows the King-dom, Reign of love and light; For it we must
3. Not a - lone we con-quer, Not a-lone we fall; In each loss or

spir - its, At the call di - vine; Gifts in dif-fering meas - ure,
la - bor Till our faith is sight; Proph-ets have pro-claimed it,
tri - umph Lose or tri - umph all. Bound by God's far pur - pose

Hearts of one ac - cord, Man - i - fold the serv - ice, One the sure re-ward.
Mar - tyrs tes - ti - fied, Po - ets sang its glo - ry, He - roes for it died.
In one liv - ing whole, Move we on to-geth - er To the shin-ing goal!

Sun High Above

GARLAND

Doris M. Gill, 1936

Alice M. Pullen, 1936

1. Sun high a - bove, sun high a - bove, Gir - dles the
2. Wind of the air, wind of the air, Car - ries good
3. Star of the night, star of the night, Spar - kles and
4. What can we do? What can we do? We would take

earth with a gar - land of love. West - ward the peo - ple are
ti - dings to folk ev - ery - where. Snow lands so fro - zen and
glit - ters with guard - i - an light. Brown fa - ces, white fa - ces
part in this bus - y world too. True help is giv - en when

wel - com - ing day, Joy - ful - ly chil - dren a - wak - en and play.
for - ests so tall— Ev - ery land prais - es the Fa - ther of all.
turn to the sky, Smil - ing in won - der at star-worlds on high.
all of us are Neigh-bors to oth - ers both near and a - far.

All the World

FRIENDSHIP

Harry Webb Farrington
Moderately, with spirit

J. Michael Haydn (1737–1806)
Adapted by Edith Lovell Thomas

1. The world came to my home one day, To spread a won-drous feast;
2. The world came to my school to-day, And brought me won-drous games;
3. The whole world came to church to-day, Their praise and gifts to bring;

The ships and planes in bright ar-ray Brought gifts from West and East;
The play-mates strange had nought to say, Nor told their stran-ger names;
In ev-ery tongue to sing and pray And wor-ship Je-sus King.

From In-di-a, spice; from Chi-na, tea, My ta-ble high to fill;
But all could laugh and play like me, Soft, warm were heart and hand,
Not as the Wise Men, rid-ing far, To find Him in one place;

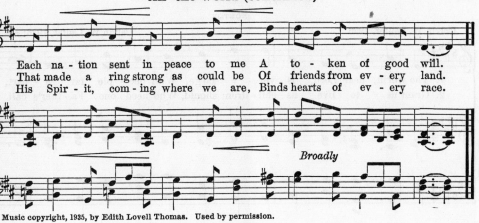

Each na - tion sent in peace to me A to - ken of good will.
That made a ring strong as could be Of friends from ev - ery land.
His Spir - it, com - ing where we are, Binds hearts of ev - ery race.

Broadly

God Loves His Children Everywhere 98

REST

Ethel Wendell Trout, 1926 Frederick C. Maker, 1887

1. It makes no dif - ference, East or West, Wher -
2. It makes no dif - ference, North or South, Wher -

ev - er we may be, God is our Fa - ther, Friend, and Guide, His
ev - er we may be, God loves His chil - dren ev - ery - where, And

gifts are showered on ev - ery side; He cares for you and me!
guards us with His ten - der care; He loves both you and me!

The Brotherhood of Man

NORTON

Calvin W. Laufer, 1926

Calvin W. Laufer, 1926; alt.

1. The world, dear Lord, is ver - y large, With peo - ple far a - part,
2. Grant us to live as chil - dren should, Who heed one Fa - ther's call

Yet all a - like, what - e'er their needs, Are chil - dren of Thy heart.
And, round a com - mon place of prayer, De - sire the good of all.

And though some live in for - eign climes, Or is - lands of the sea,
So help us serve each oth - er, Lord, What - e'er our race or clan,

One fam - i - ly tie u - nites them still And they be - long to Thee.
That through our love for each may come The broth - er - hood of man. A-MEN.

Brother of All the World

CASA BIANCA

Alice M. Pullen

Lawrence Curry, 1939

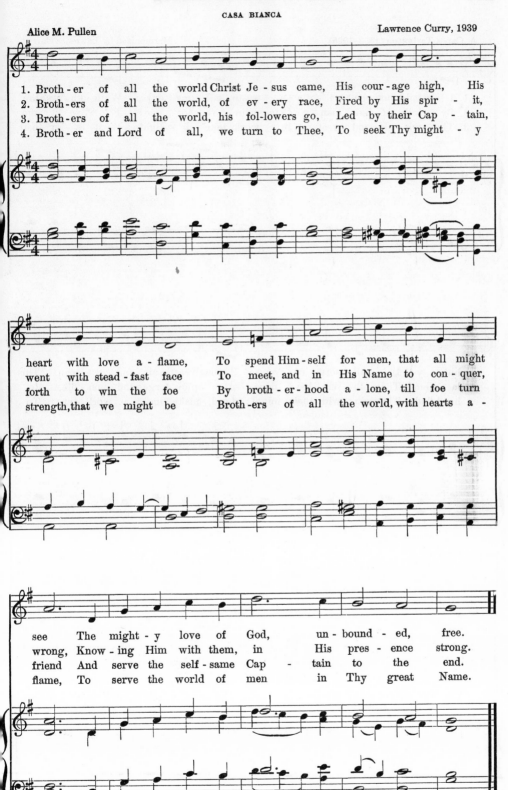

1. Broth-er of all the world Christ Je-sus came, His cour-age high, His
2. Broth-ers of all the world, of ev-ery race, Fired by His spir - it,
3. Broth-ers of all the world, his fol-lowers go, Led by their Cap - tain,
4. Broth-er and Lord of all, we turn to Thee, To seek Thy might - y

heart with love a-flame, To spend Him-self for men, that all might
went with stead-fast face To meet, and in His Name to con-quer,
forth to win the foe By broth-er-hood a-lone, till foe turn
strength, that we might be Broth-ers of all the world, with hearts a-

see The might-y love of God, un-bound-ed, free.
wrong, Know-ing Him with them, in His pres-ence strong.
friend And serve the self-same Cap - tain to the end.
flame, To serve the world of men in Thy great Name.

101 All the World's Working

CARTER

A. Capes Tarbolton (1853–1925)

Old Folk Song
Harmonized by Lawrence Curry

1. I would not be i-dle Or waste half my days, While oth-ers are
2. By toil of how man-y Comes com-fort for one: I live by the
3. The wis-est and great-est In work take de-light, What-ev-er their

bus-y In all sorts of ways: Through earth, air, and o-cean This
la-bor That oth-ers have done. At plow, forge, and spin-dle, In
hand finds They do with their might; Lord, make me a work-er, To

truth is ex-pressed, That all the world's work-ing And work-ers are blessed.
mines and at sea, There are peo-ple toil-ing Whose work is for me.
toil with good cheer, That earth may be bet-ter Be-cause I am here.

The Workers

DIX

Miriam A. Peterson

Arr. from Conrad Kocher, 1838

1. For the work-ers in the mill, For the crafts-men and their art,
2. For the toil-ers on the farm, For the sail-ors on the sea,
3. Hap-py homes where joy is shared, Well-earned rest for tir-ed hands,
4. Lord of Life, to Thee we pray, May Thy love fill ev-ery heart;

For the build-ers' read-y skill, And the trades-men in the mart:
For the min-ers' strength of arm, We shall ev-er thank-ful be.
Life a-bun-dant is the prayer Of these toil-ers in all lands.
Peace and broth-er-hood hold sway, Jus-tice rule in mill and mart.

Lord of all, for them we raise This our hymn of grate-ful praise.
Lord of all, for them we raise This our hymn of grate-ful praise.
Lord of all, for them we ask Fair re-ward for dai-ly task.
Lord of all, what-e'er man's birth, May Thy King-dom come on earth! A-MEN.

Study War No More

Negro Spiritual
Harmonized by Lawrence Curry

1. Goin' to lay down my bur - den, Down by the riv-er-side, Down by the riv-er-side,
2. Goin' to lay down my sword and shield, Down by the riv-er-side, Down by the riv-er-side,

Down by the riv-er-side, Goin' to lay down my bur - den, Down by the riv-er-side, to
Down by the riv-er-side, Goin' to lay down my sword and shield, Down by the riv-er-side, to

REFRAIN

stud-y war no more. I ain't goin' to stud-y war no more, Ain't goin' to
stud-y war no more.

stud-y war no more, Ain't goin' to stud-y war no more; I ain't goin' to

stud-y war no more, Ain't goin' to stud-y war no more, Ain't goin' to stud-y war no more.

God's Plan

104

Christian Ostergaard
Trans. by J. A. Aaberg

Danish Folk Tune
Harmonized by Lawrence Curry

1. That cause can nei-ther be lost nor stayed Which takes the
2. Each no-ble serv-ice that men have wrought Was first con-
3. There-by it-self like a tree it shows: That high it
4. Be then no more by a storm dis-mayed, For by it

course of what God has made; And is not trust-ing in walls and
ceived as a fruit-ful thought; Each wor-thy cause with a fu-ture
reach-es, as deep it grows; And when the storms are its branch-es
the full-grown seeds are laid; And though the tree by its might it

tow-ers, But slow-ly grow-ing from seeds to flow-ers.
glo-rious By qui-et grow-ing be-comes vic-to-rious.
shak-ing, It deep-er root in the soil is tak-ing.
shat-ters, What then, if thou-sands of seeds it scat-ters?

105 A Prayer for Peace

GOSHEN

Wilhelmina D'A. Stephens, 1939

German Tune
Arr. by Thomas Hastings

1. We pray Thee, O Father, that wars soon may end,
2. We seek, then, O Father, a peace that is true;
3. We pray Thee, O Father, the time be not long

And in Thy wide king-dom that friend may help friend;
May work-er and dream-er their skills now re-new,
Till si-rens and war drums be turned in-to song,

No mat-ter what col-or or race they may be,
Thy beau-ti-ful world to a-dorn and com-plete
That men, wom-en, chil-dren re-joi-cing may live

May all live in hap-py and just u-ni-ty.
With gifts that for good and not e-vil are meet.
And glo-ry to love and not ha-tred may give. A-MEN.

Blessed Is the Nation Whose God Is the Lord

Our God, Our Help in Ages Past

106

ST. ANNE

Psalm 90
Isaac Watts, 1719

William Croft, 1708

1. Our God, our Help in a - ges past, Our Hope for years to come,
2. Be - fore the hills in or - der stood, Or earth re - ceived her frame,
3. A thou - sand a - ges in Thy sight Are like an eve - ning gone;
4. Our God, our Help in a - ges past, Our Hope for years to come,

Our Shel - ter from the storm - y blast, And our e - ter - nal Home:
From ev - er - last - ing Thou art God, To end - less years the same.
Short as the watch that ends the night Be - fore the ris - ing sun.
Be Thou our Guard while trou - bles last, And our e - ter - nal Home.

America

AMERICA

Samuel F. Smith, 1832   "Thesaurus Musicus," 1740

1. My coun - try, 'tis of thee, Sweet land of lib - er - ty,
2. My na - tive coun - try, thee, Land of the no - ble free,
3. Let mu - sic swell the breeze, And ring from all the trees
4. Our fa - thers' God, to Thee, Au - thor of lib - er - ty,

Of thee I sing; Land where my fa - thers died, Land of the
Thy name I love; I love thy rocks and rills, Thy woods and
Sweet free - dom's song: Let mor - tal tongues a - wake; Let all that
To Thee we sing: Long may our land be bright With free - dom's

pil - grims' pride, From ev - ery moun - tain - side Let free - dom ring.
tem - pled hills; My heart with rap - ture thrills Like that a - bove.
breathe par - take; Let rocks their si - lence break, The sound pro - long.
ho - ly light; Pro - tect us by Thy might, Great God, our King.

America the Beautiful

MATERNA

Katharine Lee Bates, 1904

Samuel A. Ward, 1882

1. O beau - ti - ful for spa - cious skies, For am - ber waves of grain,
2. O beau - ti - ful for pil - grim feet, Whose stern, im - pas - sioned stress
3. O beau - ti - ful for he - roes proved In lib - er - at - ing strife,
4. O beau - ti - ful for pa - triot dream That sees be - yond the years

For pur - ple moun-tain maj - es - ties A - bove the fruit - ed plain!
A thor - ough-fare for free - dom beat A - cross the wil - der - ness!
Who more than self their coun - try loved, And mer - cy more than life!
Thine al - a - bas - ter cit - ies gleam Un - dimmed by hu - man tears!

A - mer - i - ca! A - mer - i - ca! God shed His grace on thee
A - mer - i - ca! A - mer - i - ca! God mend thine ev - er - y flaw,
A - mer - i - ca! A - mer - i - ca! May God thy gold re - fine
A - mer - i - ca! A - mer - i - ca! God shed His grace on thee

And crown thy good with broth - er - hood From sea to shin - ing sea!
Con - firm thy soul in self - con - trol, Thy lib - er - ty in law!
Till all suc - cess be no - ble - ness And ev - er - y gain di - vine!
And crown thy good with broth - er - hood From sea to shin - ing sea!

Our City

PATMOS

William George Tarrant, 1895

Henry J. Storer, 1891

1. The fa - thers built this cit - y In a - ges long a - go,
2. Yet still the cit - y stand - eth, A hive of toil - ing men,
3. Let all the peo - ple praise Thee. Give all Thy sav - ing health,

And, bus - y in its bus - y streets, They hur - ried to and fro;
And moth - er's love makes hap - py home For chil - dren now as then;
Or vain the la - borer's strong right arm And vain the mer-chant's wealth.

The chil - dren played a - round them And sang the songs of yore,
O God of a - ges, help us Such cit - i - zens to be
Send forth Thy light to ban - ish The shad - ows and the shame,

Till, one by one, they fell a - sleep, To work and play no more.
That chil - dren's chil - dren here may sing The songs of lib - er - ty!
Till all the civ - ic vir - tues shine A - round our cit - y's name.

Thanks for Our Town

HYMNUS URBI

Doris M. Gill, 1935

Alice M. Pullen
Adapted by Lawrence Curry

1. Come, let us re-mem-ber the joys of the town: Gay vans and bright
2. And let us re-mem-ber the cho-rus that swells From au-tos and
3. And let us re-mem-ber the life of the street: The hors-es that
4. Come, let us now lift up our voi-ces in praise, And to our Cre-
5. We thank Thee, O God, for the num-ber-less things And friends and ad-

bus-ses that roar up and down, Shop win-dows and play-grounds and
ham-mers and whis-tles and bells, From fierce-pant-ing en-gines and
pass us, the dogs that we meet, Gray pi-geons, brown spar-rows, and
a-tor a thanks-giv-ing raise For towns with their build-ings of
ven-tures which ev-ery day brings. O may we not rest un-til

swings in the park, And street lamps that twin-kle in rows aft-er dark.
clear-strik-ing clocks, And si-rens of ves-sels a-float in the docks.
gulls from the sea, And folk who are friend-ly to you and to me.
stone, steel, and wood, For peo-ple who love them and work for their good.
all that we see In towns and in cit-ies is pleas-ing to Thee!

Words copyright, 1938, by Presbyterian Board of Christian Education.
Music copyright, 1940, by Presbyterian Board of Christian Education.

111   Help Us Love Our City

FARIS

Calvin W. Laufer   Calvin W. Laufer, 1926

1. God, help us love our cit - y, Its tem - ples, homes, and schools;
2. In - spire our hearts with feel - ings Of hon - est love and pride,

The parks in which we wan - der, Their trees and friend - ly pools.
So that our prayers and serv - ice At no time are de - nied;

And grant us grace to hon - or Its pur - pos - es and laws,
But, mov - ing on and up - ward In paths our fa - thers trod,

Its stir - ring dreams of jus - tice For ev - ery wor - thy cause.
At length there shall be build - ed A cit - y un - to God.

Now Thank We All Our God

NUN DANKET

Martin Rinkart, c. 1636
Trans. by Catherine Winkworth, 1858

Johann Crüger, 1648

1. Now thank we all our God With heart and hands and voi - ces,
2. O may this boun - teous God Through all our life be near us,
3. All praise and thanks to God The Fa - ther now be giv - en,

Who won-drous things hath done, In whom His world re - joi - ces;
With ev - er - joy - ful hearts And bless - ed peace to cheer us;
The Son, and Him who reigns With Them in high - est heav - en,

Who, from our moth-ers' arms, Hath blessed us on our way
And keep us in His grace, And guide us when per - plexed,
The one e - ter - nal God, Whom earth and heaven a - dore;

With count - less gifts of love, And still is ours to - day.
And free us from all ills, In this world and the next.
For thus it was, is now, And shall be ev - er - more.

112

All Good Gifts Around Us

WIR PFLÜGEN

Matthias Claudius, 1782
Trans. by Jane M. Campbell, 1861

Johann A. P. Schulz, 1800

1. We plow the fields, and scat - ter The good seed on the land,
2. He on - ly is the Mak - er Of all things near and far;
3. We thank Thee, then, O Fa - ther, For all things bright and good,

But it is fed and wa - tered By God's al - might - y hand;
He paints the way - side flow - er, He lights the eve - ning star;
The seed - time and the har - vest, Our life, our health, our food;

He sends the snow in win - ter, The warmth to swell the grain,
The winds and waves o - bey Him, By Him the birds are fed;
No gifts have we to of - fer, For all Thy love im - parts,

The breez - es and the sun - shine, And soft re - fresh - ing rain.
Much more to us, His chil - dren, He gives our dai - ly bread.
But that which Thou de - sir - est, Our hum - ble, thank - ful hearts.

All Good Gifts Around Us (concluded)

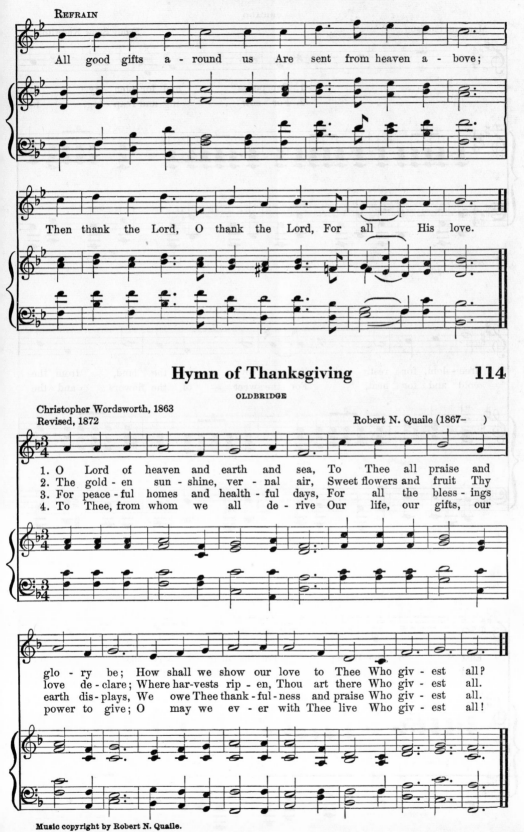

REFRAIN

All good gifts a-round us Are sent from heaven a-bove;

Then thank the Lord, O thank the Lord, For all His love.

Hymn of Thanksgiving   114

OLDBRIDGE

Christopher Wordsworth, 1863
Revised, 1872

Robert N. Quaile (1867–   )

1. O Lord of heaven and earth and sea, To Thee all praise and
2. The gold-en sun-shine, ver-nal air, Sweet flowers and fruit Thy
3. For peace-ful homes and health-ful days, For all the bless-ings
4. To Thee, from whom we all de-rive Our life, our gifts, our

glo-ry be; How shall we show our love to Thee Who giv-est all?
love de-clare; Where har-vests rip-en, Thou art there Who giv-est all.
earth dis-plays, We owe Thee thank-ful-ness and praise Who giv-est all.
power to give; O may we ev-er with Thee live Who giv-est all!

115   For Peace and for Plenty

CHICAGO

Margaret Sangster

Fanny Snow Knowlton

1. For peace and for plen - ty, for
2. For sow - ing and reap - ing, for

free - dom, for rest,   For joy in the land, from the
cold and for heat,   For the sweet of the flowers and the

East to the West;   For the dear star - ry flag, with its
gold of the wheat;   For ships in the har - bor, for

For Peace and for Plenty (concluded)

red, white, and blue,   We thank Thee from hearts   that are
sails   on   the   sea,   O   Fa - ther   in   heav - en,   our

ten - der   and true,   We thank Thee from hearts that are
songs rise   to Thee,   O   Fa - ther   in   heav - en,   our

ten - der   and   true.
songs rise   to   Thee !

116 Come, Ye Thankful People

ST. GEORGE'S, WINDSOR

Henry Alford, 1844

George J. Elvey, 1859

1. Come, ye thank-ful peo-ple, come, Raise the song of har-vest home:
2. All the world is God's own field, Fruit un-to His praise to yield;

All is safe-ly gath-ered in, Ere the win-ter storms be-gin;
Wheat and tares to-geth-er sown, Un-to joy or sor-row grown:

God, our Mak-er, doth pro-vide For our wants to be sup-plied:
First the blade, and then the ear, Then the full corn shall ap-pear:

Come to God's own tem-ple, come, Raise the song of har-vest home.
Lord of har-vest, grant that we Whole-some grain and pure may be.

DEUS TUORUM MILITUM

Alfred Tennyson, 1849

Grenoble Church Melody

1. Ring out, wild bells, to the wild sky, The fly - ing
2. Ring out the old, ring in the new, Ring, hap - py
3. Ring out false pride in place and blood, The civ - ic
4. Ring in the val - iant man and free, The lar - ger

cloud, the frost - y light: The year is dy - ing
bells, a - cross the snow: The year is go - ing,
slan - der and the spite; Ring in the love of
heart, the kind - lier hand; Ring out the dark - ness

in the night; Ring out, wild bells, and let him die.
let him go; Ring out the false, ring in the true.
truth and right, Ring in the com - mon love of good.
of the land, Ring in the Christ that is to be.

118 **Song for the New Year**

Miriam Drury

Miriam Drury, 1939

1. Once a - gain to its close Comes a year full of days;
2. As the sea - sons re - turn With their chan - ging dis - play—
3. Now a new year has dawned And its days are un - known;

Joy - ful, we sing Of Thy boun - ti - ful ways;
Day turns to night, And the night turns to day;
Christ is our Guide, We shall not be a - lone:

For the peace of our land, For a - bun - dance and cheer,
We re - joice in our homes And the friends we hold dear;
May the Spir - it of truth In our liv - ing ap - pear;

Fa - ther, we thank Thee For life this past year.
Fa - ther, we thank Thee For love this past year.
Fa - ther, be with us Through - out this new year.

O Come, Let Us Worship

119

Psalm 95: 6

Kyrie by George Elvey
Arr. by Edward Shippen Barnes, 1926

O come, let us wor - ship and bow down: Let us

kneel be - fore the Lord our Mak - er.

Arrangement copyright, 1927, by Presbyterian Board of Christian Education.

120 A Call to Worship

Psalm 100: 4, 5

Miriam Drury

Group 1

En - ter His gates with a song of re - joi - cing,

Group 2

Come to His courts with an an - them of praise;

Group 1

Be thank - ful to Him, for His mer - cy en - dur - eth;

Group 2   *All*

Praise ye the Lord, Praise ye the Lord.

rit.

Holy, Holy, Holy, Lord of Hosts

121

(Sanctus)

Isaiah 6: 3

Arr. from Gaul's "The Holy City"

Ho - ly, ho - ly, ho - ly, Lord of Hosts: Ho - ly,

ho - ly, ho - ly is the Lord of Hosts.

Music copyright by Novello & Co., Ltd. Used by permission.

The Lord's Prayer

122

Matthew 6: 9–13

Gregorian Chant

1. Our Father which art in heaven,   Hal - lowed be Thy Name.
2. Give us this   day our dai - ly bread.
3. And lead us not into temptation, but deliver us from e - vil:

Thy Kingdom come. Thy will be done in earth, as it   is in heav - en.
And forgive us our debts, as we for - give our debt - ors.
For Thine is the Kingdom, and the power, and the glory, for ev - er. A - men.

Glory Be to God on High

(Gloria in Excelsis)

Second Century Greek

Old Scottish Chant

1. Glory be to God on high: and on earth peace, good will toward men.
2. { We praise Thee, we bless Thee, we } { wor-ship Thee: } { we glorify Thee, we give thanks to Thee for } Thy great glo - ry.

3. O Lord God, heaven-ly King: God the Fa - ther Al - might - y.
4. { O Lord, the only begotten Son, } Je - sus Christ: { O Lord God, Lamb of God, } Son of the Fa - ther,

5. That takest away the sins of the world: have mer-cy up-on us.
6. Thou that takest away the sins of the world: have mer-cy up-on us.
7. Thou that takest away the sins of the world: re - ceive our prayer.
8. { Thou that sittest at the right hand of God the } Fa - ther: have mer-cy up-on us.

9. For Thou only art ho - ly: Thou on - ly art the Lord.
10. { Thou only, O Christ, with the } Ho - ly Ghost: { art most high in the glory of } God the Fa - ther. A -MEN.

Glory Be to the Father

(Gloria Patri)

Second Century

H. W. Greatorex, 1851

Glo - ry be to the Fa - ther, and to the Son, and to the

Ho - ly Ghost; As it was in the be - gin - ning, is

now, and ev - er shall be, world with-out end. A - men, A - men.

Glory Be to the Father

(Gloria Patri)

Second Century

Old Scottish Chant

Glory be to the Father, and to the Son, and to the Ho - ly Ghost;
{ As it was in the beginning, } shall be, world with - out end. A - men.
{ is now, and ever }

126 The Lord Is in His Holy Temple

Habakkuk 2: 20

Calvin W. Laufer, 1926

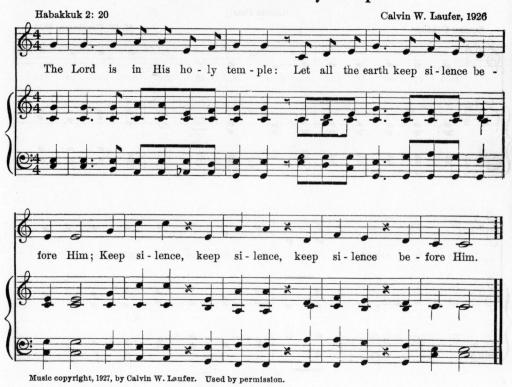

The Lord is in His ho-ly tem-ple: Let all the earth keep si-lence be-

fore Him; Keep si-lence, keep si-lence, keep si-lence be-fore Him.

127 Seek Ye the Lord While He May Be Found

Isaiah 55: 6

Calvin W. Laufer, 1926

Seek ye the Lord while He may be found,

Call ye up-on Him while He is near.

Our Gifts We Share

MEDITATION

Calvin W. Laufer, 1926

John H. Gower, 1890

128

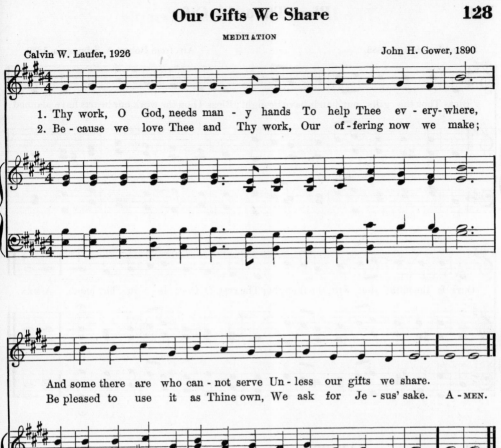

1. Thy work, O God, needs man - y hands To help Thee ev - ery-where,
2. Be - cause we love Thee and Thy work, Our of - fering now we make;

And some there are who can - not serve Un - less our gifts we share.
Be pleased to use it as Thine own, We ask for Je - sus' sake. A - MEN.

All Things Come of Thee, O Lord

129

I Chronicles 29: 14

Ludwig van Beethoven (1770–1827)

Freely

All things come of Thee, O Lord, and of Thine own have we giv - en Thee. A - MEN.

130

Bless Thou the Gifts

CANONBURY

Samuel Longfellow, 1886

Arr. from Robert A. Schumann, 1839

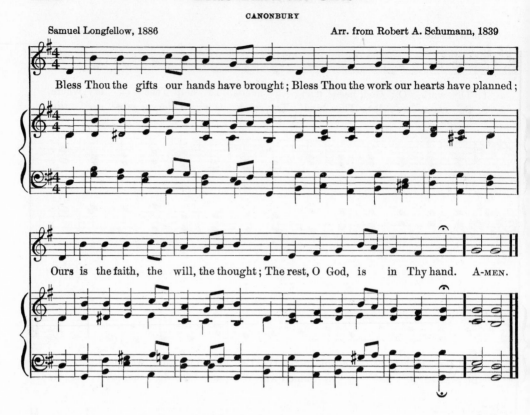

Bless Thou the gifts our hands have brought; Bless Thou the work our hearts have planned;

Ours is the faith, the will, the thought; The rest, O God, is in Thy hand. A-MEN.

131

All That We Have Is Thine

SCHUMANN

William Walsham How, 1864

Mason and Webb's " Cantica Laudis," 1850

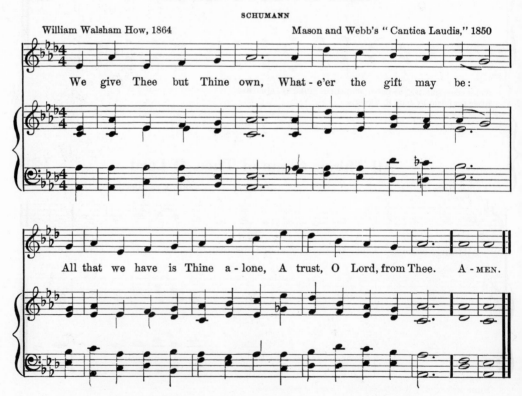

We give Thee but Thine own, What - e'er the gift may be:

All that we have is Thine a - lone, A trust, O Lord, from Thee. A - MEN.

Hear Our Prayer, O Lord

GORDON

Calvin W. Laufer, 1926

Hear our prayer, O Lord; Hear our prayer, O Lord;

Hear our prayer, O Lord, And grant us Thy peace. A - MEN.

Our Prayer

H. C. Macdougall

Psalm 19: 14

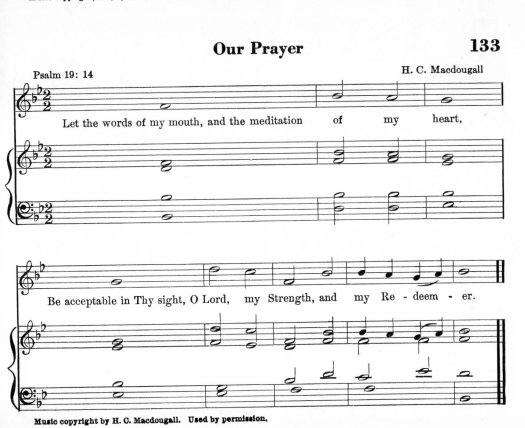

Let the words of my mouth, and the meditation of my heart,

Be acceptable in Thy sight, O Lord, my Strength, and my Re - deem - er.

Sabbath Prayer

MORECAMBE

Frederick C. Atkinson, c. 1870

O Thou who hear - est ev - ery heart - felt prayer,

With Thy rich grace, Lord, all our hearts pre - pare;

Thou art our Life, Thou art our Love and Light,

O let this Sab - bath hour with Thee be bright! A - MEN.

Keep Me, Lord

E. S. B.

Edward Shippen Barnes, 1926

Andante espressivo

Keep Thou my hands e'er swift to toil for Thee, Keep Thou my feet Thy mes - sen - gers to be, Keep Thou my thoughts e'er quick to turn to Thee in praise, Keep Thou my life, dear Lord, through all my days. A - MEN.

(*Amen ad lib.*)

136

Jacob Arcadelt
Arr. from "Ave Maria"

Ludwig van Beethoven
Arr. from Sonata, Op. 2, No. 3

138

Johannes Brahms
Arr. from "Symphony No. 3"

Antoine-Edouard Batiste
Arr. from "Andante in G"

140

Felix Mendelssohn–Bartholdy
Arr. from the Aria "O Rest in the Lord" ("Elijah")

Franz Schubert
Arr. from " Menuetto " (" Fantasia," Op. 78)

142

Georg Friedrich Handel
Arr. from the " Pastoral Symphony " ("The Messiah ")

Jean Sibelius
Arr. from " Finlandia "

Johann Sebastian Bach (Harmonizer)
"O Jesulein süss, O Jesulein mild"

145

Arr. from Negro Spritual " Were You There "

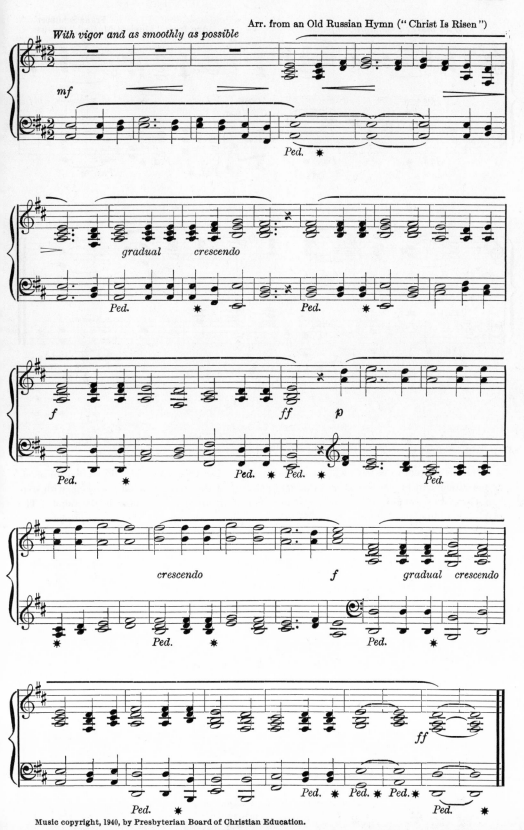

Arr. from an Old Russian Hymn ("Christ Is Risen")

With vigor and as smoothly as possible

Franz Schubert
Arr. from " Moment Musical," Op. 94

With marked rhythmic emphasis

Here is a poem to be read while the music of No. 148 is being played. In reading to music do not attempt to fit the words into the note patterns of the music. Read the poem with ease and expression, keeping the content and meaning of the words paramount in the mind. The pianist should begin playing a little ahead of the reader. The reading should end in one of two ways: either the music and reading should end simultaneously or the pianist should finish a little after the reader.

A little experimenting will quickly determine the proper speed of the music. Be sure to fit the music to the poem—not the poem to the music.

The Upward Road

I will follow the upward road today:
I will keep my face to the light,
I will think high thoughts as I go my way,
I will do what I know is right.
I will look for the flowers by the side of the road,
I will laugh and love and be strong,
I will try to lighten another's load,
This day as I fare along.

Grace Wilbur Conant, 1927
"Temper My Spirit"

SCRIPTURE FOR USE IN WORSHIP

IN WORSHIP we sing and pray, we read or recite Scripture verses or passages, we listen to music. Sometimes we "just sit quietly and let God's good thoughts come to us"; we call this meditation.

There are beautiful hymns and music and pictures in this, your book, to help you to worship or plan worship services. On this page and the next, Scripture verses and passages are listed which you can use with music and hymns in a worship service. These are grouped in sections, each section being named. As you look through the hymnbook you see that the hymns are grouped in sections which have the same names. This is to make it easy for you to find hymns and Scripture that belong together when you are planning a worship service.

As you look at the Scripture on this page and the next, you will see that there are readings to be read responsively by a reader and the Junior group. There are psalms to be read or recited together, or to be read by a leader. Sometimes you may want to type or mimeograph the Scripture readings as they are given in the Bible, so that each person has a copy. Sometimes the Scripture can be read directly from the Bible by one person, or by a leader and a group. Sometimes the part to be said by the group may be copied on a blackboard.

Section 1. "Praise Ye the Lord"

ONE way of worshiping God is to praise him. We can praise God in hymns, in Scripture, in prayer, and in our thoughts. All the Scripture in this section is in praise of God. When you are preparing a worship service of praise, you will find in the praise section of the hymnbook hymns that will go with these Scripture readings.

The Wondrous Works of God
Reader: Job 37 : 14b–16.
Group: Psalm 118 : 23.
Reader: Job 37 : 9–12.
Group: Psalm 118 : 23.

A Reading: Praise to God
Psalm 92 : 1–5a.

God's Care for All His Works
Reader: Psalm 104 : 1–5.
Group: Job 37 : 14b.

Reader: Psalm 104 : 10–13.
All: Psalm 86 : 12.

A Reading: "Praise Him"
Psalm 150.

Praise for the Lord's Day
Reader: Psalms 118 : 24; 122 : 1.
Group: Psalm 150 : 1, 2.
Reader: Psalm 146 : 2.

A Reading: A Little Psalm of Praise
Psalm 117.

Section 2. "He Loved Us, and Sent His Son"

THE Bible tells us that God loved us and sent his Son, Jesus, to be our Friend and Saviour. We want to praise God more than ever when we think of Jesus, who tells us so much about God and teaches us how to live as Christians.

When Jesus Came
Reader: Isaiah 9 : 2, 6, 7a.
Group: Psalm 67 : 3, 4.
Reader: Luke 2 : 8–14.
Group: Psalm 107 : 2.
Reader: Luke 2 : 15, 16, 20.
Group: Psalm 107 : 2.

And Jesus Said
Reader: Matthew 5 : 16.
Group: Psalm 25 : 4.

Reader: Matthew 7 : 12.
Group: Psalm 25 : 4.
Reader: Matthew 7 : 7.

A Reading: Jesus Goes to Church
Luke 4 : 16–20.

A Reading: Jesus Tells a Story
Luke 15 : 11–24.

A Reading: "He Is Risen"
Matthew 28 : 1–8.

Section 3. "Lord, I Would Follow Thee"

ONCE, as they were letting down their nets, some fishermen heard a voice saying, "Follow me." They looked up and there was Jesus. They left their fishing and became Jesus' disciples. We can be followers of Jesus too; we can try to be like him.

Lord, Keep My Thoughts
    Reader: Psalm 86 : 11a.
    Group: Philippians 4 : 8.
    Reader: Psalm 86 : 11a.

"Teach Me, O Jehovah"
    Reader: Psalm 119 : 1, 2.
    Group: Psalm 119 : 33–35.
    Reader: Psalm 119 : 73.
    Group: Psalm 119 : 105, 117.

A Reading: A Story of Neighborliness
    Luke 10 : 30–37.

And Jesus Said
    Reader: Matthew 5 : 16.
    Group: Psalm 25 : 4.
    Reader: Matthew 7 : 12.
    Group: Psalm 25 : 4.
    Reader: Matthew 7 : 7.

A Reading: "He Will Direct Thy Paths"
    Proverbs 3 : 1–6.

A Reading: Who Is Great?
    Mark 9 : 33–35.

Section 4. "Into All the World"

JESUS' love reaches out to everyone. We read in the Bible of his work among the rich and poor, the high and lowly. Those who follow Jesus' example today want to help others in America and in far lands to know and love him too.

"He Loved Us, and Sent His Son"
    Reader: Luke 2 : 11.
    Group: Luke 2 : 14.
    Reader: Matthew 3 : 13, 16, 17.
    Group: Luke 2 : 14.
    Reader: Matthew 9 : 35.
    Group: Luke 2 : 14.
    Reader: Matthew 28 : 1, 2, 5, 6a.

    Group: Luke 2 : 14.
    Reader: Matthew 28 : 18–20.
    Group: Luke 2 : 14.

A Reading: "Among All Nations"
    Psalm 67 : 1–3.

A Reading: "Among the Peoples"
    Psalm 105 : 1, 2.

Section 5. "Blessed Is the Nation Whose God Is the Lord"

THERE are so many things for which to be thankful. How happy we are to live in a country where there is peace and plenty and where we can worship God in spirit and in truth!

The Sixty-seventh Psalm

    Reader: Verses 1, 2.
    Group: Verse 3.
    Reader: Verse 4.
    Group: Verse 5.
    Reader: Verse 6.
    Group: Verse 7.

"They Shall Glorify Thy Name"

    Reader: Psalm 86 : 9, 10.
    Group: Psalm 33 : 12a.
    Reader: Proverbs 14 : 34.
    Group: Psalm 33 : 12a.

Section 6. "O Come, Let Us Worship"

WORSHIP in our churches is made more beautiful with music. It also helps us to come closer to God. In Old Testament times the people praised God in song and with musical instruments. So also today we use religious songs and music in our services. Here you will find calls to worship, Scripture, prayers, and verses to think about when we meditate in our worship.

A Call to Worship
    Reader: Habakkuk 2 : 20.
    Group: Psalm 95 : 6, 7a.

A Call to Worship
    First Reader: Psalm 100 : 1.
    Second Reader: Psalm 100 : 2.
    Group: Psalm 100 : 5.

A Call to Worship
    Reader: I Chronicles 16 : 29.
    Group: Psalms 95 : 6; 96 : 9.

"Be Still, and Know that I Am God"
    Luke 10 : 27.
    James 1 : 22.
    Psalm 19 : 14.
    Proverbs 16 : 32.
    Psalm 56 : 3.
    Philippians 4 : 8.
    Proverbs 17 : 17a.

Scripture Prayers
    Psalm 51 : 10.
    Psalm 86 : 11a.

THE JUNIOR CHOIR

IN LEAFING through the pages of this hymnal the reader will notice the wealth of material for the Junior choir. Recognizing the growing importance of this field and the prominence into which the Junior choir has come in the services of worship, the editors have attempted to include a wide choice and variety of hymns for such use. The hymns of this book, some of which are listed below, present interesting material which may be developed beyond the ordinary use in the Church School.

These hymns present opportunities to the enterprising choir leader to develop unison singing enhanced by beautiful musical effects. Boys and girls should be taught to cultivate a taste for good hymn literature and good singing. The Junior choir is an invaluable means toward this end. The children participating in such an activity not only make a vital contribution to the service but are also, through their participation, drawn into ennobling religious experiences themselves. Through their leadership in music they draw others toward these finer experiences.

By keeping all the hymns in unison they are made available to the entire school and are not limited to any particular trained group. Much music for this field which has been arranged in two and three parts is too difficult for younger Juniors. In our attempt to serve the greatest number of situations we have included only those selections which are available for use by the entire school and adaptable to development by the choir. Many of these hymns are either brand-new or else so old that our people have forgotten them. Why not introduce these unfamiliar hymns through the Junior choir? The following is a list of some hymns that would make excellent material for choir as well as general use: "All Creatures of Our God and King"; "My God and King"; "The God of Abraham Praise"; "A Jewish Festival Song"; "'Lo, the Winter Is Past'"; "Christians, Awake!"; "Praise to God in Heaven"; "When Christ Was Born"; "I Heard the Bells on Christmas Day"; "O Come, O Come, Emmanuel"; "Jesus Christ Is Risen Today"; "The Strife Is O'er, the Battle Done"; "To Thee, Redeemer, King"; "For Man's Unceasing Quest for God"; "The Lord's My Shepherd"; "I Want to Be a Christian"; "Steal Away to Jesus"; "Study War No More"; "All the World"; "All the World's Working"; "Forward Through the Ages"; "Now Thank We All Our God"; "All Good Gifts Around Us"; "Come, Ye Thankful People"; "For Peace and for Plenty"; "Our God, Our Help in Ages Past"; "The New Year"; "Thanks for Our Town."

The above list is by no means complete. Many of the hymns omitted are good material for choir use. These, however, we believe to be the best for such purposes.

You will notice that the "Amen" has been added only to those hymns which might be classed as prayer hymns or which contain lines with a definite prayer thought. It may be used with any hymn as desired.

Your attention is called to Section 6. The chants and responses in this part provide much service material for the choir. You will notice that all the two-syllable words such as "glory" or "Father," when they occur at the end of a line, are so adapted that the last syllable coincides with the last note of the chant and the preceding syllable is slurred over two notes in its measure. Thus we avoid an awkward and syncopated ending of any line. A better accent on the words of the chant is thus achieved as well.

We turn this hymnal over to you with the sincere prayer that Junior worship may be enriched through the glorious ministry of song.

140

INDEX OF FIRST LINES AND TITLES

(Titles appear in small capitals)

INDEX OF FIRST LINES AND TITLES

INDEX OF FIRST LINES AND TITLES

INSTRUMENTAL MUSIC

ALPHABETIC INDEX OF TUNES

ALPHABETIC INDEX OF TUNES

* This tune has been given the name of the hymn with which it is here used.